# CONTENTS

# ILLUSTRATIONS

Most of the maps and illustrations have been drawn by the Author. Some have been redrawn from contemporary drawings, others are based on descriptions and reports in naval and military papers and manuals. The exceptions are No 7 from a painting by John Nixon, 1806; and Nos 30(3) and 64 from the Illustrated London News, 4th September 1868 and 12th April 1845 respectively.

# ACKNOWLEDGEMENTS

This book would not have been written without the help so freely given by many people and organisations. Of the institutions, grateful thanks to those in the British Library; Public Record Office; National Maritime Museum; Ministry of Defence Library; University of Southampton (Hartley Library); Royal Archives, Windsor; House of Lords Library; Pierpoint Morgan Library, New York; and the Royal Signals, and National Railway Museums. The County Record Offices in Hampshire, Sussex and Kent, and local libraries in those areas also supplied useful and often rare information. Particular thanks to the staff at Worthing library who dealt patiently with my many requests for books and newspapers through the British Library Loan Service. Several authors kindly gave me details of their researches: Geoffrey Wilson and T.W. Holmes on naval signalling, and my publisher, Vic Mitchell on aspects of railway history. Harold Goodwin corrected the manuscript and chased up some important papers in Edinburgh, my wife Jean helped with her comments, my son Andrew used his architectural skills to improve the drawings and Norman Langridge solved all the digital problems.

# CHAPTER I

## Early Fire Signals, Smokes and Smothers

**Against all invasion they have this, to me admirable arrangement. The whole country is diversified by charming hills, and from the summits of those which are nearer the sea they sweep the whole horizon. On these summits are poles with braziers filled with inflammable material which is fired by the sentinel, if armed ships of the enemy are sighted, and so in a moment the news spreads from hill to hill throughout the kingdom.** (A Venetian aristocrat writing about England in 1596).

Surrounded by sea and beset by unpredictable weather an invasion of England has always been a risky undertaking. Although the danger was always present, a serious threat to the security of the country seldom came about more than once or twice each century. Those entrusted with the protection of the country against its enemies were well aware of the value of the sea as a deterrent and of the wisdom of defeating an enemy before his ships reached the shore. Ships and seamen were of more use in peace and war than expensive bodies of troops languishing on a long coastline against an invasion threat which seldom materialised. Apart from a general reluctance by all English governments to spend money on home defence a permanent army was disliked because of the threat it posed to their stability. A presentiment reinforced by experience of the military government imposed on the country by Oliver Cromwell in 1655.[1] It was these factors, especially the long experience of the sea as a moat only to be bridged with great difficulty, which led to the development of the King's Navy several centuries before the creation of a standing army. A military force to defend the country gradually evolved from a medley of improvised arrangements in the 17th century and only became recognised as a standing army a century later. The Duke of Wellington put the point well when he said: **The Navy was the Characteristic and Constitutional force of Britain, but the Army was a new force arising out of the extraordinary exigencies of modern times.** [2]

If then there was no permanent army, by what military system was the coast defended in the earlier centuries? At the very top responsibility for defence of the realm was invested in the Sovereign who had the right to order the means by which this was to be done.[3] The Privy Council, a group of trusted advisers close to the Sovereign, acted as a decision making body in defence matters and passed orders downwards. The Sovereign appointed Lord Lieutenants to command in each county. These were men of great influence who had gained royal favour and were of proven loyalty.[4] In their military role, for they had other responsibilities, they were generals reporting directly to the Privy Council.[5] After 1549 they could appoint Deputy Lord Lieutenants to help with their task. The military duties of the lieutenancy involved the recruitment of men (the militia), their training, efficiency, discipline, and arrangements for them to be armed and mustered in times of danger. Constables and other parish officials undertook the raising of money from taxes and loans, and enforcing the laws requiring men to do military service. The officers serving under the Lord Lieutenant were county gentlemen and landowners, Justices of the Peace and others of similar standing, some of whom formed and equipped companies from workers on their estates.[6] Mobilisation of the common soldiers of the militia was required under ancient laws; particularly 13th and 15th century statutes, by which those between the ages of 16 and 60 were obliged to leave their fields and villages and take up arms when danger threatened the county in which they lived.[7] Although invasion with the objective of conquest was rare, sporadic attacks on the coast for pillage and plunder were a continuing problem in most centuries. In times of war it was usually French and Dutch privateers, but when there was weak government, general unrest or lawlessness, raids by pirates and freebooters were common. The counties from Essex to Hampshire took the brunt of these attacks, the marauders easily crossing the Channel to capture shipping making its way towards London, or unloading at the many small harbours and beaches. If the enemy landed it was up to the local men of the neighbourhood to come together in its defence.

It was Henry IV in 1403 who acted to secure his country against invasion and ordained that a watch on the coast should be kept. As he referred to this having been done in past times he made permanent a longstanding practice which even then was ancient, stretching back 200 years to the Statute of Wynton:

**It is ordained and stablished, That the Watch to be made upon the Sea Coast through the Realm shall be made by the Number of the People, in the Places, and in Manner and Form, as they were wont to be made in Times past, and that in the same Case the Statute of Winchester be observed and kept; and**

that in the Commissions of the Peace hereafter to be made this Article be put in; (3) that Justices of Peace have Power thereof to make Inquiry in their Sessions from Time to Time, and to punish those which be found in Default after the Tenor of the said Statute.[8]

As can be seen this essential piece of early defence legislation, perhaps not surprisingly, put responsibility for its extent and execution on the shoulders of those living on the coast. A burden which was bitterly resented since they also had to meet the cost of it.

The coastline from Essex to Hampshire has numerous small harbours within easy reach of the Continent; moreover an army disembarking on the beaches was within three to five days march of London. It follows that the burden of raising an adequate force of militia and paying for it fell heaviest on the southern counties. To summon part time soldiers from their work in the villages and towns to fight an attack from the sea some form of alarm system had to be permanently in place. Thus a fire beacon became the main method used for signalling the presence of enemy ships off the coast. It was a simple but effective warning which lasted more or less unchanged for over 500 years. An Ordinance from the King as early as 1326 had advised: **men living near the sea coast were to light signals of fire or make other effective signs on the approach of an enemy.** Thus the immediate neighbourhood was alerted to the danger of attack, and those in the surrounding countryside could be mustered at pre arranged places to defend it. At the end of this chapter is a list of the instructions and orders sent from London to the Lord Lieutenants of the counties about the setting up of signals to warn of attack and invasion. Some of these orders were specific to the coast of Southern England, but mostly they were copied to all counties. The list is not complete as there will be many similar references on this subject in local and county archives. However, it does confirm that an organised system for beacon signals and watchers was always in place over many centuries. Most of the orders referred to beacons or signals of smoke and fire, but church bells, horns and tokens were also used as warning signals. There was flexibility to suit local conditions since the order by Henry IV quaintly entitled 'Watching' states the signals should be given: **in the manner and form as they were wont to be made in times past.**

Even in very early centuries fire beacons were not set up in isolation, but were usually part of a large network stretching from the coast to all parts enabling the men of the county militia to be collected into a fighting force. As the system developed some beacons were designated to pass the warning across county boundaries and to other beacon lines inland. A signal sent in this way would eventually reach London although this was not the purpose of the network. The Lord Lieutenant and his captains relied on messengers to bring exact news as to what was happening. Lambarde the Kentish historian speaks of these messengers as 'hobblers' an old military term for men riding small or light horses. Although a general alarm for raising the countryside resulted from lighting the beacons those responsible for making the right strategic decisions depended on despatches from the scene of the action.[9]    During the 16th century, and particularly when the Spanish Armada was expected, the warning system was highly organised and it is thought the   Lord Lieutenants were able to rely on upwards of 76,000 men being mustered into bands to repel an attack on the coast.[10]  The strategy adopted by the Council to defeat an invasion hardly changed over  the centuries. The navy as the first line of defence was to attack and prevent a landing. If the enemy got ashore the beacons would be fired and the men would assemble with their weapons at assembly points decided upon by their commander, the Lord Lieutenant. They would then be marched to the coast to fight. An order from Edward VI in 1548 puts it succinctly: **when the beacons give warning ...ye send forth or prepare yourself to go with men  for the defence of the sea coast, as before you set forth these men must be most able, well furnished and weaponed, and also eight days vittels (food) or money with them to serve for that time.**

Tides and  weather conditions in the North Sea and English Channel meant that the most suitable time to invade was during the summer months. Reminders for the coast to be watched and the beacons manned were issued between May and September and as the cost was borne by the maritime counties, they expected this obligation to be called off when the winter came. Hence one request in December 1636 **...to cease watching this winter quarter as it is troublesome to this poor county.**[11]

If the visibility was good the fire or smoke from a lighted beacon could be seen over a wide area, but a limiting factor was that the signal could mean anything from a ship being sighted to an army actually landing. Attempts were made over the years to redefine the warning by using several beacons to give different types of warning and by nominating the lighting of others to indicate the widespread nature of the attack. Thus, if one beacon was lit no men need be mobilised; if smoke from two were seen, the enemy had landed and men inland should be mustered and marched to the coast. Some beacons on hills were expected to act as a marker for others in the valley or on a flat coast. Another variation required three beacons to be lit if the ships came within four miles (6Km) of the coast and if the enemy appeared in greater strength than could be resisted. Instruction as to the code to be used was decided centrally in London, but there was a limit to the number of interpretations which could be  be used without causing confusion locally. Several factors, wind direction and visibility, contributed to the misreading or interpretation of smoke or fire signals and where many beacons made up the signal the greater was the risk of this happening.

False alarms were a continual problem, as well as a costly nuisance if the militia were mustered and sent to the wrong place. They affected the credibility of the defence measures and were much more of a worry to the leaders than any lack of diligence by men watching on the coast. The Council sent many cautionary notes to the Lord Lieutenants asking them to tighten the authority given to magistrates and local commanders responsible for giving permission for the beacons to be lit. One Saturday in July 1545 following a written despatch about the French landing in Sussex the Kentish beacons were fired. The militia were fully mustered by the Sunday and set forth for the coast, but on reaching Uckfield they were turned back the alarm being false. A similar incident happened a month later when the beacons across Hampshire were lit causing the men in the nearby counties of Oxfordshire and Worcestershire to be mobilised. On the third day of their march to Portsmouth they were turned back as there was no danger.[12] When beacons on the Isle of Wight and at Portsmouth were wrongly fired in 1560 the warning reached as far inland as Berkshire before it was stopped for lack of confirmation. On this occasion the watchmen were reprimanded. The Portsmouth beacons were fired in error again in 1579 when they acted on a column of smoke which was subsequently found to be huntsmen attempting to destroy a badger set.[13] A more serious incident occurred in the summer of 1586 when to distract attention from the robbery of houses and further their aims supporters of recusants fired beacons in Hampshire. Most of these men were imprisoned in London.[14] False alarms were taken seriously and investigated to prevent a re-occurrence. That is why Nicholas Gilmour of the village of Charing in Kent was appointed 'scoutmaster' and put in charge of all the beacons in that county. His orders included: **... and for the avoidance of trouble and raising the country without cause it shall be lawful for you to enjoin all men...to forbear the making of fire, flames, smothers and smokes, or ringing of bells in any such place as shall be near to any beacons, or may give cause to the county to suspect that they are fires, tokens or signals to raise the county.**[15]

Another cause of false alarms was the burning off of fields of stubble and furze and in 1619 this action by a Sussex farmer led to the county beacons as well as those in Kent being fired.[16]

The place of the fire beacon in the history of the South Coast lasted as described until the end of the 18th century and the beginning of war with the new French Republic. There was fear of a major French invasion in 1797, but this came to nothing. In 1803 when war with France was resumed after the Peace of Amiens invasion seemed inevitable and extensive measures to put the coast into a state of defence were undertaken. This resulted in not only a reorganisation of the beacon stations and the way they were financed and controlled, but also their integration with other warning systems devised to warn of attacks from the sea.

# A CHRONOLOGY OF EARLY SIGNALLING ON THE COAST

These references to beacons and signals in the mainly southern counties confirms that for over six centuries an organised warning system of coast signals existed to mobilize men of the counties to fight an invader.

1324   A report of an Inquisition (enquiry) into the defences of the Isle of Wight mentioned 31 beacons said to have been "as of old". Edward II also issued orders for beacons of timber to be built on the coastline and hills of Portchester. HFC p.253-255.

1325   Orders were given to the Sheriff of Southamptonshire (Hampshire) for beacons to be erected and watchmen and sentries appointed. HFC p.256.

1326   Edward II sent orders to the Sheriffs of Kent and the other maritime counties for watches to be established where formerly one had been kept: **that the said watch would give a sign of fire or other effective means which can be seen from afar, so that the men of the neighbourhood may be able to betake themselves to the fire or other signal, in the night if need be....** K p.79.

1337   Edward III wrote to Hampshire and most other counties asking for signals of fire to be made if foreigners in galleys and ships were seen. The orders referred to the keeping of wards and watches and the placing of new and repair of old beacons in suitable places: **as has been the custom of old.** HFC p.257.

1377   Richard II in the first year of his reign orders the Sheriffs of Kent and Essex to erect beacons on the shores of the river Thames to safeguard the sea approaches to London. Two beacons were to be lit and horns sounded, whereupon the men of the county were expected to take up arms. H p.3.

1450   The Corporation of Lydd in Kent recorded payments for the cost of watching the beacons, and the delivery of broom as fuel. K p.93.

**1468** Edward IV issues orders for beacons and watches to be established because of his fear that an attack would be made by sea after the end of a truce with France. K p.81.

**1486** Fearful that an anticipated conflict between France and Italy would result in naval action on the English coast Henry VII ordered the beacons to be reinstated. HFC p.258.

**1534** Thomas Cromwell, Chancellor to Henry VIII referred to the Privy Council the question of the repair of beacons throughout the realm. K p.82.

**1536** A rebellion in the north of England led to beacons being fired in Lincolnshire and Yorkshire. K p.84.

**1539** Charles Marillac, French Ambassador to London, wrote to the Constable of France about the efficient system of beacons, guards and watchers which gave a warning to the entire country when foreign vessels were seen. Thomas Cromwell told Henry VIII that some Sheriffs had repaired their beacons while others had been negligent. The Earl of Hampshire said of the inhabitants of the Isle of Wight that: **....they keep the beacons they have set up on every hill right well.** K p.82: HFC p.259.

**1544** The Privy Council sends orders to Hampshire to erect two beacons from the Downs to the Isle of Wight to convey speedy news of enemy ships. Guidance was also given about watchers and the firing of beacons. HFC p.259.

**1545** A representation of the town of Brighton in a drawing of this date depicts an inland beacon and one on the coast, both dissimilar. The beacons are lit, the town being under attack from the French. P p.25. Instructions from the Privy Council to all the southern maritime counties contain details of the order in which beacons both on the coast and inland are to be lit when the enemy is seen, and procedures for mustering the men of the area to fight. HFC p.260.

**1546** The Privy Council writes to all Sheriffs, Commissioners and Justices giving comprehensive instructions for the working of the beacons. Later in this year the system appears to have been stood down and the watchers discharged. HFC p.260.

**1547** During the summer the beacons were still being kept up because those near Holy Island in Northumbria were fired. SPD.

**1548** Because of expectation of a French invasion in support of Scotland references to beacon watching abound. During February the boy King Edward VI ordered the Sussex beacons to be watched from 6th March until further notice. In May the Sheriffs and Justices were reminded to ensure the beacons were set up and maintained and this order was repeated in June. SPD and HFC p.262.

**1558** Fears of a French invasion led to the issue of orders for the beacons on the Kent coast between Folkestone and Lydd to be repaired and manned, and the defences got ready. SPD.

**1559** Instructions were sent to the Earl of Arundel, Lord Lieutenant of Sussex, about defence matters and these included orders for the beacons and watchers to be ready. SPD.

**1560** Orders were given at Winchester to Lord St John dealing with the detailed procedure for firing one or several beacons when a number of ships were seen, and the need to make signals so that men from the counties of Hampshire, Wiltshire, Dorset and Sussex could be assembled into an army. HFC p.263.

**1566** Payments for building and watching the beacons at Eltham, Kent appear in the accounts of the churchwardens between 1566 and 1574. K p.94.

**1570** In October the Privy Council informs Lord Cobham the Lord Lieutenant, that the beacon watch in Kent can be discontinued. K p.87.

**1572** In December Elizabeth I says that beacon watching can be discontinued until further notice. SPD.

**1573** A manuscript note on the page of a book which has since been lost refers to letters and orders for the firing of beacons being in use between 1544 and 1573. SPD.

**1574** Further orders from the Privy Council to Lord Cobham at the end of November told him to discontinue the beacon watch in Kent. K p.87.

**1580** The Sheriff of Hampshire is told in December that because of the sharpness of the weather he can stop the beacon watches until he receives further orders. HFC p.264.

**1585** All the Lord Lieutenants in the country are ordered to have the beacons watched and the beaches guarded. SPD.

**1586** The Privy Council asks Hampshire for a report of the condition of the beacons in the county. SPD.

**1587** Nicholas Gilmore of Charing is appointed by the Privy Council to be Scoutmaster (officer responsible) for the beacons, watchmen, and arrangements for building, repairing, and lighting the Kent beacons. The Council also added to the orders already issued for the circumstances in which the beacons were to be fired. K p.20 and SPD

**1588** The Spanish Armada actually arrived off the Isle of Wight on 4th August, but a week earlier when the ships had been spotted as they passed Land's End, the alarm must have been sounded from Kent to

Hampshire for the Privy Council noted the names of men and captains who had gone to Portsmouth " for the aid and relief of the town upon the firing of the beacons". K.p.89 and SPD.

**1590** Orders are sent from the Privy Council in October for the beacons to be put up again. SPD.

**1595** The counties ask the Privy Council for permission to discharge the beacon watchers because of the lateness of the season. SPD.

**1596** Intelligence reports from the Continent suggested that Spain might attempt revenge for her defeat at Calais in 1588 and although it was October the Privy Council ordered the reinstatement of the beacon watches. A month later quite elaborate arrangements were made for gunfire and beacons to give the alarm along the Kent coastline should enemy ships be seen to approach the Thames and Medway rivers. K p.90.

**1598** Beacons were fired in Yorkshire on account of frequent raids by privateers coming from Dunkirk. SPD.

**1599** The Privy Council issued instructions in August for beacons on the coast at the mouth of the Sleeve to be watched. SPD.

**1600** In April orders were sent to Kent and Essex for the beacons to be watched and lit if galleys from Spain were sighted. A beacon was to be built near the remains of Queenborough Castle in the Isle of Sheppey with two men on duty every night. SPD.

**1613** The Justices said that the beacon on Netley Heath, Hampshire was to be repaired. HNQ p.107. Beacons were also built in Northumberland during this year because of a threat from attacks by Spanish ships. EM p.212.

**1625** The continuing war with Spain and France led to fears of invasion on the Sussex coast. The Deputy Lieutenants renewed their warrants annually for beacons to be repaired and watches kept up during the summer months. They also decided many disputes between parishes over responsibility for manning and payment of the beacon watches. S p.191-2
In Hampshire the Privy Council asked the Deputy Lieutenants to ensure that the trained bands were ready for action when the beacons were fired. HFC p.265.

**1628** Two beacons were lit at Rockford Hundred in September because of the appearance of privateers from Dunkirk. Just before Christmas Day the Lord Lieutenant was told that a hostile enemy was expected to land on the Hampshire coast and the trained bands should be ready to march when the beacons were fired. The procedure for beacon watches was also reviewed. SPD.

**1629** A note was made in the State Papers that the old orders for firing the beacons were inappropriate. In September the justices of east Kent reported that a survey of the beacon and defence measures was to be undertaken. SPD.

**1630** In June, it was reported in Devon that the beacons had been placed in the charge of gentlemen of the neighbourhood who visited them every night. Firing was not permitted unless they gave permission. In October the cost of watching the Essex beacons during the summer was £80. SPD.

**1639** There was dissatisfaction amongst the inhabitants of Buddlesgate Hundred in Hampshire who complained that they had always repaired the beacon on a hill at West Bere with wood from the forest. The wood was now owned by Sir William Waller who had started legal actions to stop them cutting wood. They wanted Sir William either to allow them to continue, or to explain his actions to the Council. SPD.

**1640** A note appears in the State Papers about the beacons being made ready and duly watched. In September the Deputy Lord Lieutenants confirmed their diligence in the condition and watching of the Hampshire beacons. In October Devon reported that their beacons would be repaired, and watched by two men by day and three at night. They were not fired unless the Constable gave his consent. SPD.

**1651** Revised orders were sent to the Isle of Wight giving the Captain of the island authority to fire the beacons. Not only was he to ensure that the beacons were well watched, but a sufficient quantity of wood was to be held nearby to replenish them. The alarm was also to be sounded by ringing the church bells. SPD.

**1652** Following the outbreak of the Anglo Dutch war and the arrival in August of the Dutchman Admiral Van Ruyter off the Brighton coast the beacons were fired to alert the neighbourhood. VCH p.158.

**1659** The fire beacon and hut for the watchmen at Hawkhurst, Kent were said to be derelict. K p.91.

**1672** Sir J. Williamson, a courtier and M.P. for Rochester wrote to Viscount Brouncker, (Lord High Admiral) to say that King Charles II wanted beacons to be set up at various suitable places between the South Foreland in Kent and Lee near Greenwich. Their purpose was to signal the approach of enemy ships up the Thames towards London. SPD.

**1745** War appeared imminent and in expectation of an invasion from the French Channel ports some partial reinstatement of the beacons along the South Coast may have been undertaken. K p.91.

## Sources

HFC    White H.T. The Beacon System in Hampshire*
Hampshire Field Club Papers, Vol. X, 1926-27

K    White H.T. The Beacon System in Kent*
Archaelogia Cantiana, Vol. XLVI, 1934.

H    Hasted E. Hist. & Topographical Survey of Kent,
Vol. IV, 1798.

P    Parry J.D. Historical & Descriptive Account of the Coast of Sussex, 1833.

SPD    Calendars of State Papers (Domestic). Public Record Office.

HNQ    Alarm beacons of Hampshire*. Hampshire Notes &
Queries, Vol. IX, 1898.

EM    Boynton L. Elizabethan Militia, 1558-1638. 1980.

S    Fletcher A. Sussex 1600-1660, 1980.

VCH    Victoria County history of Sussex, Vol 2. 1973.

* Primary sources are given in these publications.

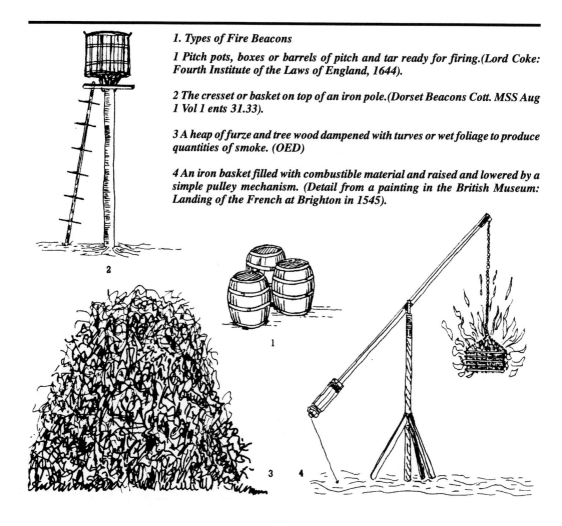

*1. Types of Fire Beacons*

*1 Pitch pots, boxes or barrels of pitch and tar ready for firing.(Lord Coke: Fourth Institute of the Laws of England, 1644).*

*2 The cresset or basket on top of an iron pole.(Dorset Beacons Cott. MSS Aug 1 Vol 1 ents 31.33).*

*3 A heap of furze and tree wood dampened with turves or wet foliage to produce quantities of smoke. (OED)*

*4 An iron basket filled with combustible material and raised and lowered by a simple pulley mechanism. (Detail from a painting in the British Museum: Landing of the French at Brighton in 1545).*

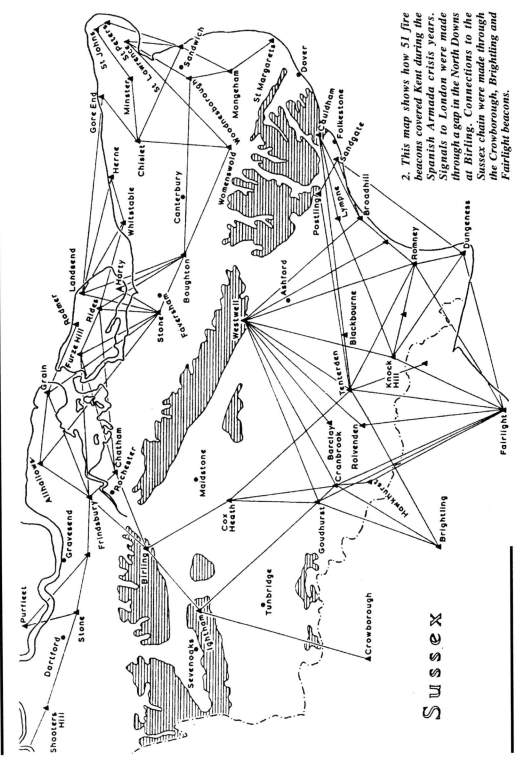

2. This map shows how 51 fire beacons covered Kent during the Spanish Armada crisis years. Signals to London were made through a gap in the North Downs at Birling. Connections to the Sussex chain were made through the Crowborough, Brighling and Fairlight beacons.

*3. A stretch of 20 miles (32km) of the Sussex coast in 1587 showing the beacons and defences between Newhaven and Pevensey Haven. The signal was passed from the coast inland to beacons at Firle and along the range of the South Downs which come down to the sea at Beachy Head near Eastbourne.*

**4. A stretch of 15 miles (24km) of the Sussex coast in 1587 showing the beacons between Littlehampton and Shoreham. The beacons stand in pairs and signal to the interior of the country through those on the Highdown, Cissbury and Chanctonbury hills of the South Downs.**

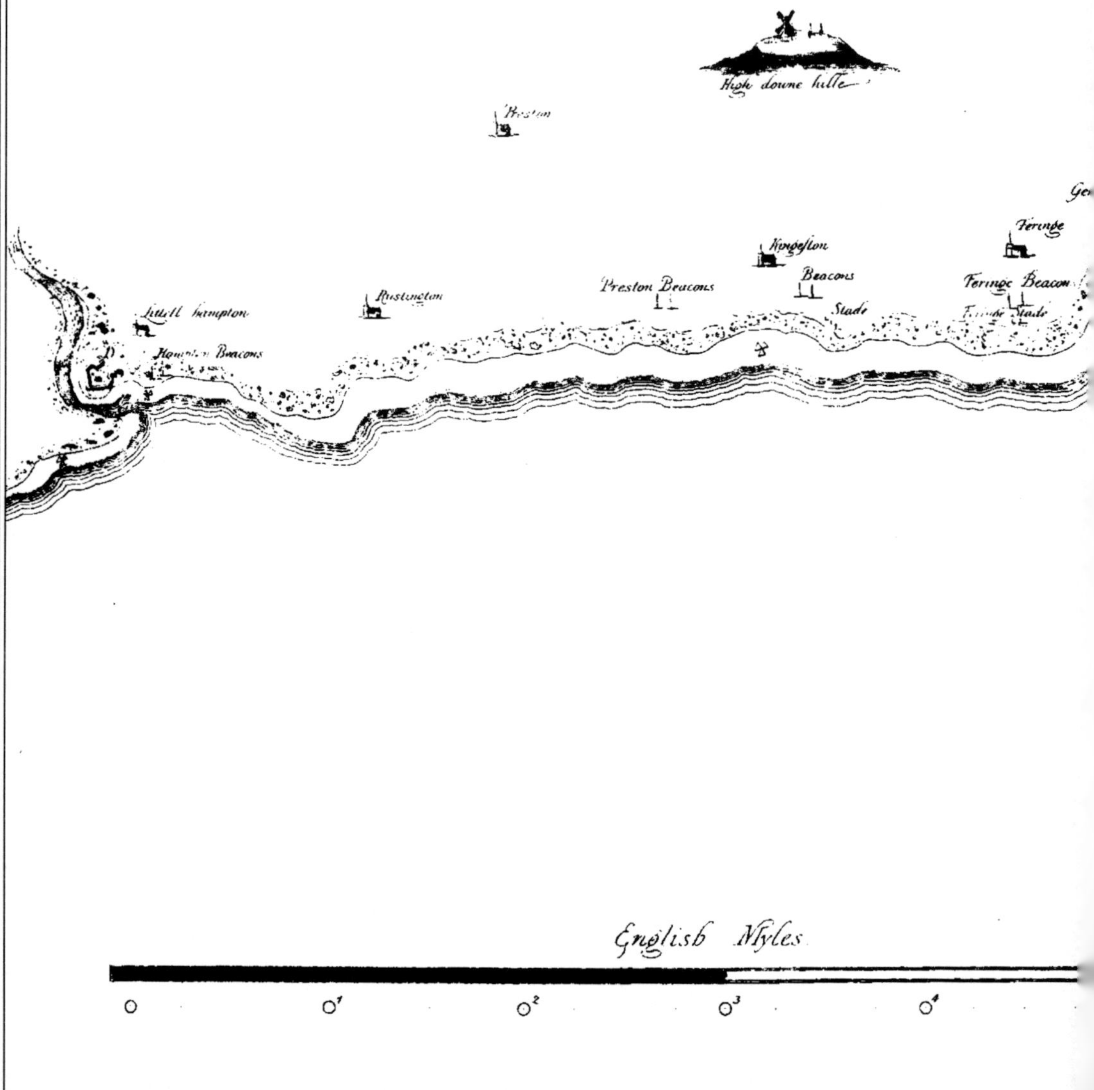

*High downe hille*

*Preston*

*Ger*

*Feringe*

*Kingston*

*Beacons*

*Feringe Beacon*

*Rustington*

*Preston Beacons*

*Stade*

*Littell hampton*

*Feringe Stade*

*Houniton Beacons*

*English Myles*

○    ○$^1$    ○$^2$    ○$^3$    ○$^4$

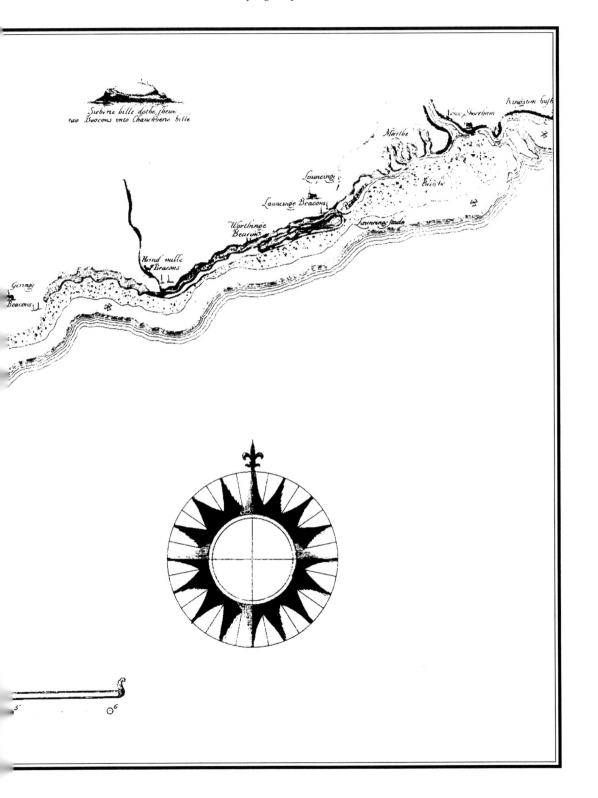

5. *Most of the defences in the 16th century were paid for by those living in small communities close to the coast. A contemporary report describes them as a line of zig zag trenches dug in places where the defenders had some height advantage over an enemy landing on the shore. When the beacons were lit these strong points were manned by the men of the district armed with pikes and muskets.*

# CHAPTER 2

# The First Admiralty Land Signals

**Communications dominate war: they are the most
important single element in strategy, political
or military.** (Admiral Mahan, 1900)

Wars act as a spur for change and never more so than when the safety of the country is at stake. Projects turned down as being too costly in peacetime suddenly become affordable and are wanted overnight.

Those admirals given the task of guarding the Channel coast have always been faced with a problem of deciding where the enemy was and how they could bring their ships to battle in time to thwart his plans. A shortage of crews and ships as well as unpredictable weather added to their difficulties. Against this unchanging background officers with practical experience of policing the Channel came to realise that a chain of signal posts sited along vulnerable stretches of the coast could increase their knowledge of the whereabouts of enemy ships. By keeping in touch with each other and naval patrols offshore those manning the signal posts could plot the course of the enemy and alert the nearest military command. There was no great novelty about a system of this sort, but it required organisation, co-operation and trained staff as well as resources from the Admiralty budget which were not to be forthcoming until the danger of invasion threatened.

It was during the French wars of the late 18th century that references to a rudimentary and piecemeal system of land signalling along the South Coast first began to appear in Admiralty records. During the summer of 1745 fears of a French invasion of Kent in support of a Jacobite rebellion in England and Scotland reached a peak. Admiral Edward Vernon, known as 'Old Grogram-breeches' was given a small force of ships to patrol an area near Deal. As well as seeking information about French intentions from the many small vessels going up and down the coast he arranged for signals to be displayed on land if the French fleet was seen. He wrote to John Norris, the captain in charge of Deal Castle, and asked him to write to all the churchwardens of seaside parishes between the South Foreland and Beachy Head asking them to display a signal if French ships were sighted. If by day a flag was to be hoisted from the church steeple and at night a fire was to be lit in an iron pot hung in the same place.[1] In return he promised to order his cruisers to fly a jack-flag at their topmost head if they spotted the French at sea so that the seaside villages could be warned. He expected the French to embark from Calais and Boulogne and try to land on Dungeness and his advice to the Deputy Lieutenants in the county was to ask for volunteers to take up arms and assemble at Swingfield Minis north of Folkestone. More than 4,000 men were said to have responded, but the invasion was called off and the men returned to their homes. Another early instance of ship to shore co-operation happened in 1781 when Admiral Sheldon applied to the Admiralty for a special allowance to pay two petty officers to keep watch on the top of Maker church tower which commands a splendid view of Plymouth Sound. Their orders were: **to obtain material information of occurrences in the offing.** On the chalk cliffs of the South Foreland near Deal overlooking a busy area of sea known as the 'Downs' Sir Edward Hughes who commanded the naval squadrons on patrol got permission to build a shed: **for one of his commissioned officers to be established with flags to keep a lookout.**[2] These shore based signal stations were of course cheaper than asking for more ships and crews, but they were set up at this date only on the initiative of one or two admirals.

In the manner in which the army fought its battles overseas it had little need for signals and yet it was the Duke of Richmond, when Master General of the Ordnance, who was instrumental in pushing the Admiralty case for a comprehensive system of coastwise signals. This came about because of Parliament's concern over the best method of protecting the naval dockyards at Portsmouth and Plymouth. George III appointed a board of naval and military officers under the chairmanship of Richmond to report on what should be done, and the committee's terms of reference were broadened to include any other measures which would help to repulse an enemy attack on the coast.

The Duke completed his report in June 1785, and it included a recommendation: **that a set of signals be established on the projecting headlands with intelligent mariners to make them, as of essential advantage in conveying early intelligence of the approach of an enemy, and for the protection of commerce.**[3] Some copies of this report had a list of possible sites for the signal posts, but for security purposes these had a restricted circulation and none appear to have survived in the public archives. The most important part of the

Duke's report was about the building of extensive and costly fortifications at the naval dockyards. Although these were badly needed in the circumstances of the time, the arguments against were put with such force when they were discussed by Parliament in May 1786 that the finance measure to fund them was defeated by the casting vote of the Speaker. Without the urgency of any imminent attack on the country there was no political will to spend money on a danger that might never materialize, although political intrigue and dislike of the Duke may have contributed to the rejection of his Committee's proposals. Whatever the reason the opportunity to have a system of signal posts along the coast was lost and the idea was to languish in the background of naval thinking for its time to come.

The outbreak of war with Revolutionary France seven years later renewed apprehensions about the condition of the coast defences and the need for a coast signalling system was revived. Although the French navy was not at first a serious threat the Admiralty found themselves stretched to keep up patrols in the Channel and also maintain their commitments overseas. Without further discussion money was found from the naval budget and orders were issued for huts and signal masts to be built on suitable sites between the Isle of Wight and Land's End. The minutes of the Board of Admiralty meeting on 27th March 1794 recorded the decision laconically: **It being deemed expedient that flagstaffs shall be erected**,[4] suggesting that the need was so obvious as to need no explanation.

The decision to build this first line of signal posts west of the Isle of Wight also helped to resolve another of the Admiralty problems which was how to gather intelligence about attacks by privateers swooping across the Channel to capture or destroy commercial shipping heading for London.

The Admiralty entrusted the work of planning and building the signal posts to Captain Clements of the sloop **'Spitfire'** and apart from some sketchy guidance he was told to get on with it and report progress. It is clear that he interpreted his orders to mean that the signal posts were to be built so that they could communicate with those adjacent which meant that they had to be within sight of each other whether built on high ground or along a flat shoreline. Within three months the worthy Captain Clements had completed his survey and in August he was told to extend the line of posts eastwards from the Isle of Wight to the North Foreland near Margate.[5] Meanwhile the Navy Board, (the works arm of the Admiralty) got on with procuring the necessary building materials and the masts, furnishings and equipment. These were assembled at Portsmouth dockyard before being delivered to the sites by ship.

Admiral McBride was then in charge of the naval base at Plymouth. He had been a member of the Fortifications Committee which under the Duke of Richmond had proposed a system of signal posts in 1785 and doubtless because of his experience he was now ordered to prepare: **draft instructions for the guidance of the signal lieutenants yet to be appointed and to send these to the Admiralty for approval.**[6]

Throughout 1795 the Navy Board was continually being pressed to hasten completion of the signal posts along the most invasion likely stretch of coast between Portsmouth and Kent. Not only had the need for them to be up and running become more urgent but the Admiralty were anxious to extend the system up the East Coast of Britain.[7] By late April most of the posts along the South Coast were ready although inevitably problems arose over their operation in some places. Most complaints came from the lieutenants in charge and were about difficulties in reading the signals from adjacent signal posts. Captain Clements reported to the Admiralty that he cleared these by inspecting the daily journals kept by the officers. If he found that signals had been acknowledged in hazy weather, snow or rain he merely dismissed them as inconsistent. However, in Kent and Sussex there were difficulties of a different kind. The signals sent from west to east could be easily seen, but when they were sent the other way they were less clear because of a backdrop of high ground which made it difficult to distinguish the outline and position of the flags on the mast. To improve visibility, Captain Clements recommended in a report written in April 1795 that he should be authorised to build four additional posts. He wanted one between Fort Cumberland (Portsmouth) and Selsey, and a second between Selsey and Beaconsfield. The latter was later renamed Middleton which is on the outskirts of Bognor. Another was to be between Worthing and Whitehawk Hill at Brighton, and the fourth was between Dungeness and Folkestone. Despite his assurance that these posts could be set up immediately because the necessary materials were already available at Portsmouth dockyard some accounts give completion dates of a year later. There was no delay over approval from the Navy Board, but difficulties in agreeing rents and land leases may have been a stumbling block.

During his survey of sites for the signal posts it soon became apparent to Captain Clements that it would be possible to use the naval signalling system to pass information of the enemy's intentions to the many military encampments along the South Coast. As he explained in his report the extra posts: **will admit of the signals being conveyed with much greater accuracy to the encampments on the coast should their Lordships' think proper to give directions for this purpose.**[8] It seems unlikely that their Lordships' had thought about closer liaison with the military in this context and subsequently they were cautious if not unhelpful in agreeing to pass on information as we shall see. However, to Captain Clements and those military officers he had met on the coast the advantages were clear.

Once the chain of signal posts was completed the Admiralty were reluctant to build any more even where visibility remained poor. However, on one occasion they responded quicker. This was when General Don, in charge of the garrison on the Isle of Wight asked for a signal post to be set up on a hillock in Parkstone Forest close to his headquarters.[9] It was thought that the French might be preparing to land on the island before mounting an attack on Portsmouth. Parkstone was an ideal site. It was close to the barracks which were built shortly after 1760 where the prison now stands.[10] News of enemy movements could be signalled from all points of the island: Ashey Down 6 miles ( 9.5km) away; St Catherine's Down 9 miles ( 13km); and Needles Down in West Wight which was 11 miles (16km) distant. The Ashey Down post was built at first on the crest of a long stretch of downs 426 feet(130m) high and is sometimes named as Nunwell Down suggesting there were two signal posts close to each other. This is not so as annotations to some of the Admiralty lists confirm. The confusion arose following a decision to re-establish the post in June 1803 after the resumption of war with France. Joseph Bettesworth writing from Lewes Barracks demanded an exorbitant rent for the use of his land on Ashey Down. Mr Vass wrote to Sir Charles Saxton at Portsmouth Dockyard to suggest that a site on Nunwell Down two miles east of the former signal post site would be equally convenient. Moreover, Sir William Oglander, the owner was agreeable if his tenant, Mr Kent, was paid rent of one guinea a year. Sir Charles agreed and so from the summer of 1803 the old Ashey Down post stood on Nunwell Down where it was equally visible to the island posts already mentioned and also to Fort Cumberland (Portsmouth) and West Wittering in Sussex.[11] The need for the Parkstone post was supported by Colonel Brownrigg at the War Office and the Admiralty ordered it to be built without delay. It was ready by January 1801 and Lieutenant Hewitt was put in charge. For a different purpose further changes to communications with the Isle of Wight were attempted a few years later. During the summer of 1805 the Navy Board commissioned Mr Goodhew, an inventor of a system of flag signalling similar to Popham's Telegraphic Code, to survey the route for a line of signal posts from Portsmouth to and across the Isle of Wight. This would entail using existing signal posts where possible and building new ones. Admiral Montague who commanded at Portsmouth suggested that one post could be put on Fort Monkton or on the ravelin at Portsmouth harbour. Across the Solent on the Isle of Wight new signal posts were actually built at Wootton and on top of Mottison Down. From here the messages were to be signalled via the Needles to an intermediate station on Hordle Cliff near Lymington on the mainland. The intention was that this would shorten the distance of making signals along the mainland coast which had always been difficult in this area. Mr Goodhew said that the most tedious part of his job was negotiating the purchase of land for the signal houses. This is not surprising because some landlords were less than sympathetic to Admiralty demands on account of the time it took to get payment. However, by the end of the year the route was far from complete and Mr Goodhew was told to stop his work and send in his accounts. The new signal stations were auctioned off, the Admiralty deciding that they wanted instead to concentrate their resources on the new shutter telegraph they were building from from London to Plymouth.[12]

During the twenty years of war the coast signal system was in use the Navy Board received many complaints from ships and inspecting officers about the 21 mile (32km) gap between the signal posts at Beachy Head and Fairlight near Hastings in East Sussex. The long distance led to signalling problems with ships in parts of Rye Bay or those standing off Dungeness. Captain Rolls and Captain Schomberg of the Sea Fencibles pleaded from 1805 onwards about the danger to convoys from French privateers which could speed across the Channel to capture and wreak destruction before the defences could be alerted.[13] Admiral Berkley, in charge of all the signal posts and Sea Fencibles said that the lieutenant at Beachy Head had told him that he had been unable to receive any signals from the Fairlight post for fifteen months. The Admiral commented...**an entire stop is put to the communication of signals westward which in the event of the enemy sailing from Boulogne to the westward might be attended by the most fatal consequences.**[14] Despite this observation from a very senior and respected Admiral no action was taken possibly because of the cost involved. Then, four years later, after serious attacks on a convoy the Admiralty acted and agreed to the building of two intermediate signal posts between Beachy Head and Fairlight. Even this decision turned out to be controversial. To save money Captain Rolls suggested that the signal masts could be put on top of two Martello towers, but the Board of Ordnance rightly objected claiming that it would interfere with the traverse of the 24 pounder guns. It was then decided to build a new post on Galley Hill at Bexhill, and to use Langley Fort near Eastbourne for the other. But the fort was found to be unsuitable and a site at Wallsend, Pevensey was chosen instead.[15] Both these signal posts were not ready until 1811, and there was a last minute attempt to do without the one at Wallsend because some cruiser captains queried whether it was really needed. As the building was already completed, it was decided to take it into service. The chain of signal posts along the South Coast was eventually extended to cover most of the coast of Great Britain. Although it was only a wartime measure, it achieved some permanency because of the long time the conflict with France lasted. First manned for action in 1795, signalling continued until the temporary Peace of Amiens, when they were closed down suddenly on 22nd April 1802.[16] The men were discharged and the sites returned to their owners.

However the peace was to last only eight months and when war broke out the following year the Admiralty had to issue orders for the signal system to be set up again. [17] Mr Vass from Portsmouth dockyard and his counterpart at Chatham then repeated the laborious business of arranging for the land to be leased and the signal stations to be repaired, or rebuilt where they had been demolished. Meanwhile, the Admiralty reappointed the lieutenants to take charge and recruited the men. Within a matter of weeks most of the signal posts were in working order again. They then continued in service more or less unchanged until the end of the war with France in 1814. Closure instructions were issued in November of that year and the stores and equipment were collected by naval ships **Prince** and **Rosario** from 7th December. The signal staff was paid off just before Christmas, an economical, but heartless action which left some homeless and without a job and doubtless many regrets that the war had ended.[18]

Even this was not quite the end of coast signalling, for the Admiralty were reluctant to give up a communication system which had served them so well and which would have to be established again in a future war. Six months later they decided to rebuild the then derelict signal posts with a line of new semaphore stations. This venture, which began with promise in Kent and Sussex, had an eventful history, but an untidy end many years later.

*6. A warning system to alert the coast agreed between Admiral Vernon's ships in the English Channel and the army commander at Deal Castle. Communication was by signal flags hoisted on church steeples and a Union Jack flown from the topmast of the cruisers.*

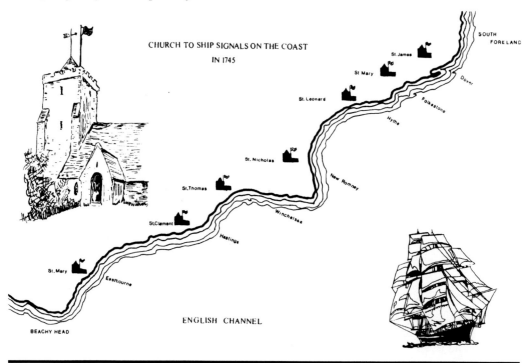

*7. A contemporary painting of the Admiralty signal post on Ashey Down near Brading, Isle of Wight. It was established in 1795. The view shows the Sea Mark on top of the down.*

*8. A view of the Admiralty signal post established in 1795 on the top of Seaford Head, Sussex. The signal being flown is No 11 : An enemy ship or vessel, close under land. Martello tower 73, the last in the South Coast chain was finished in December 1807. Based on a drawing by a visitor from Cumberland in September 1811.*

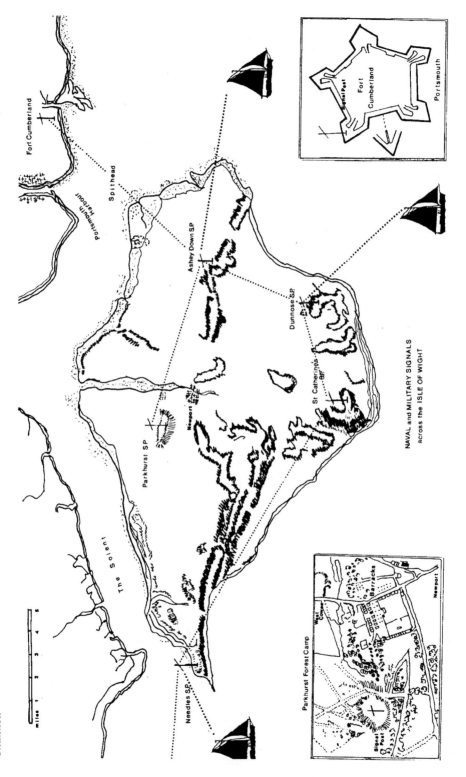

9. General Don's headquarters and camp for the defence of the Isle of Wight was close to Albany Barracks at Parkhurst. Following his request the Admiralty included his headquarters in their signal network so that warnings of the approach of an enemy would reach him from ships in the English Channel.

# CHAPTER 3

# Setting up the Naval Land Signal Network

**You are to confider the great object of eftablifhing thefe Pofts, is that no Ship or Veffel of the Enemy fhall be able to approach the Coaft without being difcovered to be fuch from one of the Pofts;...(from Admiralty orders to a newly appointed lieutenant in charge of a signal post.)**

For an adequate watch of the English Channel from Kent to Cornwall, the Admiralty estimated that about one hundred signal stations were needed. These had to be built, equipped, and staffed with officers and men trained to use new signal codes which had yet to be devised. Quite an undertaking given the need for each station to be carefully positioned in relation to its neighbour, and when no survey of the coast for the purpose existed. Moreover the programme had to be carried through quickly, and in the event was completed and working in just under a year.

Two men were given a key role in undertaking this task. Captain Clements commanding the sloop **Spitfire** was responsible for surveying the various sites, and Mr Nicholas Vass, a master house carpenter from Portsmouth dockyard, supervised the construction work. As an experienced master mariner Captain Clements used his navigational skills to select the sites for the signal masts so that the flags would be visible over long distances. He was also expected to negotiate with landlords and tenants to secure the most favourable leases on the land needed. His orders were to agree the lowest rent possible, the only concession being that the landowner would be allowed to keep the signal house for his own use when it was no longer needed.[1] Some public spirited men, perhaps acutely aware of the importance of protecting their land against the French, offered it free of rent to the Admiralty, but others were less accommodating and haggled over terms and conditions.

In one of several reports to the Admiralty, Captain Clements explains how he selected the site for a signal station by choosing the position for the mast only after raising a pole 30 feet (9m) high at the next signal post so that he could be sure the signals could be seen from it. This was sometimes difficult when trees or a dark backdrop of high ground obscured the sight lines. The land distances over which the signals were expected to be seen varied from 6-22 miles (9-32km), and to keep the masts clear of any obstruction they had to stand about 80 feet (24m) high.[2]

The sloop **Spitfire** was the base for building operations and Mr Vass lived on board with Captain Clements. It travelled along the South Coast dropping off materials and stores at the various sites, which were often in places difficult to reach by lane or highway. Mr Vass carried with him a plan of the signal house for which parts had been prefabricated at Portsmouth dockyard. He was responsible for its erection using a small workforce of masons and carpenters which he recruited from nearby towns. Both the captain and Mr Vass seem to have achieved a good working relationship for Captain Clements speaks well of him in the log which he kept: **that as far as I can be allowed to judge Mr Vass attended to his instructions and made them** (the signal stations) **as comfortable as the situation and size admit of.** There is a hint here that the basic plan had some limitations even to sailors used to roughing it at sea, but more of this later.

It was on 27th March 1794 that the Admiralty decided that work should start on the signal stations between the Isle of Wight and Land's End and from April until October Captain Clement and his crew were busy with this task.[3] However, he had to move fast because on 13th August he was ordered to extend his survey eastwards and add to the line between Hampshire and Kent.[4] By the end of 1794 the Admiralty were calling for weekly reports on the progress of stations between the Isle of Wight and North Foreland as they were anxious to extend the system up the eastern coastline of Britain.[5]

As the success of the signal line depended on the decisions made by Captain Clements he was probably a much harassed sailor as he and his men toiled their way along the coast in winter, landing their cargo of flags, masts, ropes and hut sections as near as they could get to each signal site. As he reports back to the Admiralty: **these stores were delivered in the same presentation as I received them from Portsmouth Dockyard,** which suggests that not all were in first class condition. There is a note later from the lieutenant at Dunnose (Isle of Wight) complaining that although he had got a new pennant the signal balls were very bad and he had had to patch them up so that they would last throughout the winter.[6]

When the **Spitfire** anchored off a convenient beach the crew unloaded the mast and stores and manhandled them up the cliff or across the marshes to the site chosen for a new signal station. The first task was to sink the heel of an old ship's topmast into the ground. The mast was 50 feet (15m) high and fitted with a cap, crosstrees and fid. To this was clamped a flag staff 30 feet (9m) long which was fitted with a truck and two sleeves for the ropes. A yard, or gaff of another 30 feet (9m) was then added from which the signals could be suspended. To tie the mast down to the ground and give it stability as well as to raise and lower the signals a lot of rope was needed much of it very heavy.

As much as 200 yards (182m) of 1½ inch (38mm) rope and 150 yards (46m) nearly twice as thick, had to be carried from the boat to the site.[7]

While Captain Clements supervised the positioning and erection of the signal mast Mr Vass and his workmen dug the foundations and knocked up the accommodation. On the Isle of Wight he engaged Mr Wellington and Mr Chapel from Newport to build the signal houses at St Catherines's Point and Ashey Down, and at the Needles in Western Wight Mr Grove and Mr Braden travelled from their homes in Yarmouth.[8] The specification for the signal accommodation written by the Navy Board was spartan and given the exposed positions in which it was likely to be built unlikely to be comfortable.

It was described as a temporary building with rough wooden sides which stood on a small plinth of stones or flints. The most flimsy feature was the roof which was made up of 163 square yards (136sq.m) of canvas stretched over the sides and fastened down to supports with scupper nails. It is perhaps not surprising that before long some of signal houses began to leak badly following exposure to the weather. Within a year of being erected the Lieutenant in charge of the post at Dunnose (near Shanklin) was complaining that his roof still leaked in every shower, and the smoke from the fire made living inside intolerable even though he had fitted a cowl to the chimney.[9] The remedy recommended by the Navy Board was to paint the roofs and walls with a mixture of tar and oakum onto which fine sand was thrown.[10] The cost of each station varied slightly from place to place, but worked out at about £127.

Contrary to what might be expected the signal houses were built so that none of the observation windows faced directly out to sea. The lieutenants complained to Captain Clements about this feature, but he dismissed their concern and explained to the Admiralty: **At present the windows of all the signal houses on the coast are placed in such a situation near as possible to look towards the next station to the eastward and westward of themselves it being felt more advisable to do so than to place them to the southward which would render the house immediately colder in winter from the prevailing southerly wind.**[12]

Inside, the signal house was divided into two main rooms. One was for the use of the lieutenant in charge and the other for three seamen. The officer's room was furnished with a deal table and chairs, sleeping cot and a bath stove, with irons and a fender for hot water.

The seamen had similar furniture and a fire grate for cooking and heating. To sleep they slung hammocks as they did on board ship. Some plans show an extra room in which signal balls and flags were kept, but this was in later signal huts built to replace those destroyed by the sea or badly affected by the weather.

Each lieutenant was issued with a brass telescope in his personal charge. It was described in the inventory as a two foot (610mm) glass, with achromatic lenses intended to minimise colour abberations. Messrs P and J Dolland of 59 St Paul's Churchyard, London had a contract with the Admiralty to supply these telescopes at a cost of two guineas.[13] Captain Lloyd of the Lincolnshire Sea Fencibles complained to the firm in 1804 about their indifferent performance. He was told that the telescopes issued for the officers in his district were similar to those supplied to other stations and were no different in clearness and magnification. He was also advised that there had been other similar complaints and where the distances were great he should either use one of their more expensive models costing £3.68, or a longer 3 foot (914mm) telescope priced at 6 guineas. These longer telescopes were in use in the semaphore stations between London and the coast and were said to be very satisfactory for there had never been any complaints.[14]

Many signal posts stood on high hills in isolated places with no fresh water close by. Thus seamen had to go daily to fetch water from the nearest farm well, or as at the Fairlight (Hastings) station from a spring said to have been some distance away. The sanitary arrangements were as rudimentary as they were in the rest of the country. A privy hut 3 x 3 feet (.836sq.m.) was standard for the officer and was built away from the living quarters. It is unclear whether this was also used by the men, but an order from the Committee of naval accounts placed a limit of £5.25 on expenditure for this purpose.[15] In area the signal house and the mast occupied half an acre of land. The Navy Board took a cost conscious view that because the men were always on duty and could drive off sheep and cattle, fencing was unnecessary. Where this did not always work in practise the seamen were expected to dig a shallow ditch around the site and use the earth to form a small embankment to keep out intruders.[16] The land taken by the Admiralty was rented from the landlord or tenant farmer, apart from the Galley Hill (Bexhill) and Cumberland Fort stations which stood on land already owned by the Board of Ordnance. Where land was rented the rents ranged from nil to £25 a year.[17] Under the terms of the leases signed by Captain Clements when the land was no longer wanted the signal houses became the property of the owner or tenant. This arrangement was to result in some disputes when the war ended and several lieutenants found themselves homeless.

When the Peace of Amiens was signed with France in August 1802, the coast signal system which had been in operation for seven years was shut down immediately and the men disbanded. As mentioned earlier, in May of the following year the war resumed and in a flurry of activity the system was re-established. An inspection by Mr J. Bower a master carpenter from Chatham dockyard found that only minor repairs were needed to the Kent signal posts, although the one on the North Foreland had to be rebuilt. Mr Vass found similarly in Sussex, but on the Isle of Wight the houses at Ashey Down, St. Catherines and Needles Point had been removed and sold by the land owner. New houses had to be erected urgently. Mr Vass reported later that because there was a shortage of canvas and the season had been so wet he authorised the roofs of the new houses to be tiled.[18] It was during negotiations over leasing the land for the resumption of re-occupation in 1803 that the Navy Board found the lack of legislation to acquire the land compulsorily a great hindrance. One or two landlords raised objections over giving up their land, or demanded an unreasonably high rent. A recalcitrant owner could of course jeopardise the continuity of the entire signal chain, and so when semaphore stations along the coast were planned a decade later, an Act permitting the compulsory purchase of land was passed through Parliament first.

During the long war with France the Navy Board letter books bulged with complaints about the state of the signal houses and the discomfort of living in them. It was usual for the officers in charge to write directly to the Navy Board and not to the captain of the district Sea Fencibles who was their direct superior. Curiously, any request for equipment and supplies had to be agreed by the captain first. That the signal houses were roughly built and draughty is not surprising given the speed at which they were put up.They also reflected the Treasury's economical approach to temporary wartime projects. Even so life for the men may have been easier than that afloat which was also uncomfortable as well as much more dangerous. Many complaints were about dilapidations caused by the weather, cramped living space, and the general misery of living day by day on exposed beaches and windy hill tops far from the society of villages and public houses. This was compounded by the need for constant watching which kept the few men tied to their post almost as if they were at sea.

At Fairlight (Hastings) Lieutenant Waters found the building untenable in winter and added a more substantial room paying the expense of £60 himself. Such modifications seem to have been acceptable provided the Navy Board were not asked to pay for the work. Even this sometimes gave rise to disputes when the officer moved out. When Lieutenant Woodger took over the Folkestone Cliff post he complained that he had been asked to pay £10 for an extra room which had been added by Lieutenant Rose, the former tenant, who threatened to pull it down if he did not comply.The Navy Board said it was to remain and no payment was to be given in return. One unlucky officer was Lieutenant Goldfinch at the Seaford station who asked if he could build a small room to have greater privacy.[19] He was told that all the signal huts were built to the same plan and if it did not suit his health to live there he should give up the job to someone else. The officer at Beachy Head had more luck. He asked to be allowed to sleep in Eastbourne during winter and was allowed to do so although we are not told what his men did.[20] At the low lying Dungeness post in 1803-4 Lieutenant Corsellis found that visibility in severe weather was very poor. He recommended putting his lookouts on the top floor of the lighthouse. The Admiralty consulted Trinity House and permission was granted.[21]

After an inspection of the Beaconsfield signal post (at Middleton near Bognor) in 1804 Admiral Berkley reported that it was being undermined by the sea and must be moved. Before this could be done it was blown away in a gale and a brick house was put up on a new site nearby.[22] The same year Lieutenant Symonds at the adjacent station of Pagham asked for shutters to be fitted to his windows to keep out sea spray in rough weather. Later it was found that this post was unlikely to survive another winter as rough seas came right to the door and guns on a nearby battery had already been moved further back.[23] It might be expected that to mitigate the cold, damp and dark living conditions the Navy Board would have been fairly generous with the fuel allowance. But this was a continuing grievance and there were many representations for it to be increased. Eventually the coal allowance was increased from four to six chaldrons a year; amounts approximating from five to seven tons. At the same time the annual candle allowance for lighting was changed from three to nearly five pounds in weight.[24]

The last signal post to be rebuilt before the war with Napoleon ended, was on the seaward slope of Whitehawk Hill to the east of Brighton. Mr Vass had reported that it was in so bad a condition that it should be knocked down and replaced by a brick house. Lieutenant Harrington who was in charge was ordered to get three estimates from local firms. This he did and a tender for £297 was accepted from Mr Pink, a Brighton builder. This sum was to be offset by £9.65 to be realised from the sale of salvaged materials from the old signal house.[25]

The signal huts were built during 1794-5 and it seemed unlikely that it was ever expected that they would last so long in places exposed to severe weather blowing directly off the sea. However, when the line was surveyed in September 1815 to consider to what use it should be put now that the war had ended, most of the 26 signal posts between the North Foreland and the Isle of Wight were found to be in a reasonable condition. Those that had been rebuilt or repaired were described as being very good. At Shoreham, Pagham and Dunnose the buildings had already gone, probably removed by the landowners as soon as hostilities ended.[26]

# Admiralty Signal Posts
## North Foreland to the Isle of Wight
## 1795 - 1815

| Signal Post & Year Opened | Location | Distance from last post | Height above the sea |
|---|---|---|---|
| **KENT** | | | |
| North Foreland* 1795 | On North Cliff at Broadstairs. | 4miles/6km | 70ft/21m |
| East Hill 1795 | Above Hope Bay between Ringwould & St Margarets. | 12miles/19km | 250ft/76m |
| Little Cornhill 1795 | On South Foreland 3km east of Dover. | 4½miles/7km | 350ft/107m |
| Folkestone Cliff 1795 | On the Eastwear Bay cliff top near the Dover road turnpike. | 6miles/10km | 150ft/46m |
| Lympne 1796 | A few metres north of Lympne Church on the heights above the Dymchurch marshes. | 7½miles/12km | 300ft/91m |
| Dungeness Point 1795 | On the point itself. | 10½miles/17km | Sea level |
| **SUSSEX** | | | |
| Fairlight 1795 | At 'Firehills' east of the town of Hastings. | 13½miles/22km | 350ft/106m |
| Galley Hill 1811 | On top of the cliff east of Bexhill. Site now under the sea. | 7½miles/12km | 50ft/15m |
| Wallsend 1811 | Southeast of Pevensey Castle; on the coast at Pevensey Bay. | 6miles/10km | Sea level |
| Beachy Head 1795 | On top of Beachy Head west of Eastbourne. | 4½miles/7km | 450ft/137m |
| Seaford 1795 | Within an earthwork on top of Seaford Head. | 6miles/10km | 284ft/87m |
| Hawk Hill 1795 | South of the racecourse on Whitehawk Hill at the back of Kemp Town, Brighton. | 10¼miles/16km | 400ft/122m |
| Shoreham 1796 | On top of the down south of Erringham Farm. | 7½miles/12km | 250ft/76m |

| | | | |
|---|---|---|---|
| Worthing<br>1795 | On the shoreline east<br>of Heene road, Worthing. | 6miles/10km | Sea level |
| Kingston<br>1795 | On the beach to the east<br>of Sea Lane. | 3¾miles/6km | Sea level |
| Beaconsfield<br>1795 | Destroyed by the sea and<br>rebuilt 1804 at end of<br>Sea Lane, Middleton-on-Sea. | 6¾miles/11km | Sea level |
| Pagham<br>1796 | On the east side of the<br>old harbour entrance. | 6miles/10km | Sea level |
| <u>Selsey Point</u><br>1796 | On the shoreline near<br>the point of the Bill. | 3¾miles/6km | Sea level |
| West Wittering<br>1796 | At the western end of<br>the Strand. | 6½miles/10km | Sea level |
| <u>Cumberland Fort</u><br>1795 | Within the fort which<br>stands on the western<br>side of Langstone<br>harbour, near Eastney. | 6miles/10km | Sea level |

## ISLE OF WIGHT

| | | | |
|---|---|---|---|
| Ashey Down++<br>1795 | Near the Sea Mark on top<br>of the hill at the back<br>of Brading. | 9½miles/15km | 425ft/130m |
| Dunnose<br>1795 | Near the tumuli on top<br>of Bonchurch Down at<br>Ventnor. | 5miles/8km | 717ft/219m |
| <u>St Catherine's</u><br>1795 | Close to the 1785 light-<br>house on the hill above<br>Chale. | 5miles/8km | 237ft/72m |
| <u>Needles Point</u>+<br>1795 | Uncertain site, but<br>probably near the<br>1859 battery. | 12miles/19km | 400ft/122m |
| Parkhurst Forest<br>1801 | On the ridge west of<br>Camp Hill prison at<br>Newport. | 6miles/11km | 272ft/83m |

## Notes

The 'Principal' signal posts are underlined.

* Communicates with the Margate signal post the next one to the north east.

+Communicates with the Christchurch Head signal post the next signal post westwards.

++ Also accepted signals from the Parkhurst signal post.

10. A sloop similar to the one sailed by Captain Clements. A one masted vessel the main sail of which was attached to the gaff above and a fixed boom spit below. Armed with ten cannon, but perhaps not more as it was laden with stores and equipment to build several signal stations.

11. Sections of the signal hut were prefabricated in the naval dockyard and along with other stores were unloaded from the Spitfire onto a beach close to sites chosen by Captain Clements.

*12. The signal hut with its lookout porch and canvas and tarred roof. A small privy hut for the Lieutenant stood a short distance away at the back.*

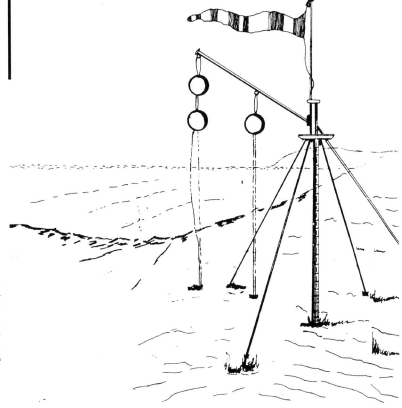

*13. A mast 80 feet (24m) tall was sunk into the ground on the highest point of the site, usually within 100 yards (91m) of the signal hut. The mast was secured with heavy ropes to hold it steady in coastal gales.*

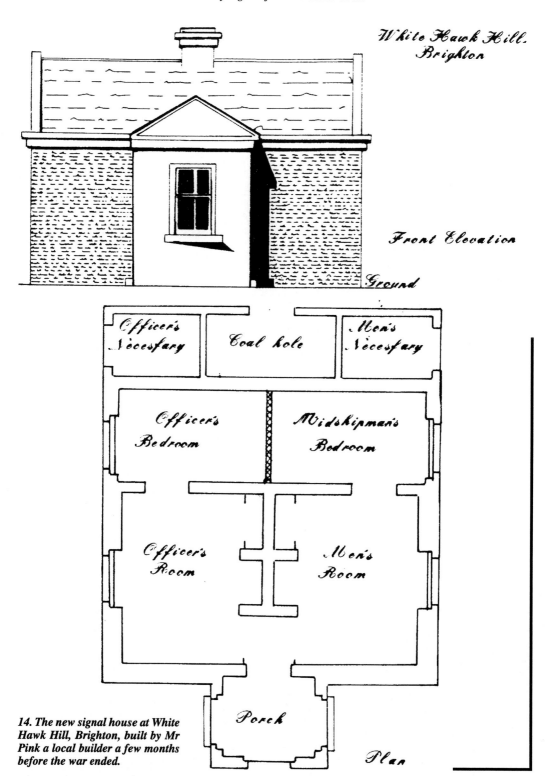

*White Hawk Hill. Brighton*

*Front Elevation*

*Ground*

*Officer's Necessary*

*Coal hole*

*Men's Necessary*

*Officer's Bedroom*

*Midshipman's Bedroom*

*Officer's Room*

*Men's Room*

*Porch*

*Plan*

**14. The new signal house at White Hawk Hill, Brighton, built by Mr Pink a local builder a few months before the war ended.**

# CHAPTER 4

# Life and Work in the Naval Signal Stations

**You are to discharge your midshipman and men; and yourself as soon as these instructions have been complied with. We are your affectionate friends...**
**(Close down letter from Admiralty Commissioners to Signal Station Lieutenants December 1814.)**

The expansion in the size of the Royal Navy during the Revolutionary war with France was dramatic. Between 1793 and 1800 the number of ships of all classes increased from 498 to 767 and officers and men from 45,000 to three times as many.[1] Included in the latter were those needed for the signal stations: a minuscule number for the entire coast from Kent to Cornwall was serviced by fewer than 600 rather less than the total required to crew one third rate warship. From this viewpoint the Admiralty decision to invest in a system of coast stations which could watch out for and give warning of the approach of an enemy invasion fleet 25 miles (40Km) offshore was tactically sound and economical in ships and manpower.

At a board meeting in May 1794 the Lords of the Admiralty approved the staffing establishment for the chain of signal posts.[2] Letters of appointment, signed by their Lordships, with instructions about how the posts should be worked were sent to each lieutenant who had been chosen from the many applying for the job.[3] The orders instructed him to: **engage one intelligent Petty Officer and two trusty men to assist you if not already procured.** His joining instructions emphasised that he was not to leave his station without permission, neither was he to allow more than one of his men to be absent at the same time, and then only for up to 24 hours. The Admiralty really looked upon the job as being similar to that of an officer afloat, except that he was in overall charge of watchkeeping throughout day and night. As he had only a single room in the signal hut any family had to live elsewhere. In later years some families managed to join their husband, but this seems to have been done without permission and usually where the officer had added to the signal building at his own expense. The Admiralty view was that the signal posts were naval stations on shore and the sailors were subject to the same rules and naval discipline as those on ships.

The purpose of the signal post was to ensure that no ship passed without being challenged and that enemy ships were identified and their course plotted. The lieutenant was told the procedure for challenging, what action to take when an enemy vessel was identified, and how to receive and pass on information from adjacent signal stations by day and night. The responsibility for teaching the lieutenant how to use the signal codes rested with Captain Clements who had supervised the setting up of the stations.[4]

All signals sent and received had to be recorded in a hand-written journal with reports on the state of the wind and the weather, and a copy was to be despatched weekly to London to arrive at the Admiralty on the following Wednesday. When disputes arose, and there were many, as to whether naval ships were keeping a good lookout when they did not respond to a challenge from the signal post, a check was made with the vessel's log book.

It was usually lieutenants without a ship and ashore on half pay who applied to be put in charge of a signal post. If appointed he had to surrender his half pay and in return he got 25p and 15p a day subsistence. This was similar to the pay for a lieutenant in the Sea Fencibles, (a coastal defence service similar to the World War II Home Guard), but although the accommodation on an isolated site was free, albeit less than comfortable, the officer would almost certainly be on continuous duty.

Payment for a Petty Officer was the same as that for a fourth rate midshipman (£1.67 a lunar month) with a subsistence allowance of 10p daily. An ordinary seamen earned only 10p a day and this was paid weekly. The lieutenant was responsible for paying the wages and for any other expenses connected with running the signal station. He was allowed a standing imprest of £30 which was reimbursed when he sent an account of his expenditure to the Admiralty each month. Rates of pay remained unchanged throughout the life of the signal post.[5]

For the first two years of their existence, the signal posts were managed directly from the Admiralty in London. But with an extension of the system to the east coast of the country and a decision early in 1798 to create a new force of Sea Fencible volunteers, the command structure was changed. From 21st March 1798 the senior captain of the Sea Fencibles was given responsibility for all the signal posts in his district.[6] This was a logical and sensible solution to the problem posed by the expanding size of both services. It also enabled the Sea Fencible captains to co-ordinate communication between the military and the navy. The captains were expected to make regular visits to each signal station to check that proper watches were being kept and the correct signals made. They also handled matters involving staff discipline and irregularities referred to them for resolution by the Admiralty. One matter which was taken very seriously was where it was suspected that the secrecy of the signal codes had been compromised by carelessness.

At all times the lieutenant was held responsible for the safety and good order of the signal house, mast, and the flags and signal balls which had to be carefully stored away when not in use. The balls were actually hoops 3 feet (1m) in diameter. They were covered by canvas and painted black and were made to a standard size and pattern suggested by Lieutenant Twisden who was in charge of the Golden Gap signal post in Dorset.[7] Included in the equipment of the station were two items of particular value. One was the brass telescope and the other was a set of special signal codes used for identifying and communicating with naval ships, but more of these later. The Admiralty was very positive about the importance of these and on taking up his post the lieutenant's orders said: **You will receive herewith a Copy of the Private Signals which are to be delivered to the King's Ships, by which they are to make themselves known to the different Signal Posts; and you are most strickly enjoined and commanded not to communicate them to any person whatever, except to such Officers as may be sent to relieve you by Us, but to keep them carefully concealed, that the Enemy may not come to the knowledge of them.**[8] Breaches of orders to keep the signals secret were taken seriously by the Admiralty and officers were disciplined even if it was found that they had allowed seamen access to the codes. The Admiralty's concern can be appreciated in view of the work required to change the codes throughout the Navy if they were thought to have been compromised.

There was no shortage of lieutenants making applications to be put in charge of signal posts. In 1793 the number of lieutenants in the navy was 1408. By 1803 this had risen to 2461 and by the end of the war 3210.[9] Despite this expansion in commissioned officers and the enhanced wartime chances of promotion and 'prize money' for those at sea, a safe job ashore had great appeal. But many of those applying were already ashore on half pay, getting on in years and frequently unsuitable for sea service because of bad health or disability. For example, the officer put in charge of the station at Kingston near Arundel in Sussex had only one arm.[10] Lord Vincent, who commanded in the Downs, is said to have appointed a lieutenant who had suffered a stroke which had affected his arm and left him with only one good eye.[11] Perhaps these were exceptions although it is known that loyal service and patronage got some officers a posting even if they were not quite up to the standard wanted of signal officers. Similarly the midshipmen, of whom there was one at every post, were either youths or seamen approaching middle age and unlikely to achieve further advancement.

There was also no problem in filling the fewer vacancies for captains put in charge of the districts. These officers were usually content to give up their half pay status for a bigger daily allowance and expenses. However, the job seems to have carried less status than that of a captain at sea, moreover, to the dissatisfaction of many there was almost no chance of any further promotion. This was never openly stated, but it was an implied restriction confirmed by correspondence from a senior admiral in 1801. Replying to a letter from the Earl of Portsmouth Lord St Vincent wrote: **the list of officers (for promotion) so far exceeds that of ships that one third of the captains and commanders must have been without employment had the war continued.** The Earl, however, continued to press the case for the preferment of a Captain Festing of the Sea Fencibles and Lord Vincent spelled out his refusal in more definite terms: **I cannot possibly agree with your Lordship that a person sitting quietly by his fireside and enjoying very near a sinecure during such a war as we have been engaged in, has the same pretension to promotion with the man who has exposed his person and hazarded his constitution in every clime.** He went on to say commanding the Sea Fencibles was not an impediment to promotion, but in his view he felt such candidates would be at the bottom of the list.[12]

A scrutiny of reports received in the Admiralty gives some idea of the kind of problems which arose in the day to day management of the signal stations. During the summer of 1797 Lieutenant Halstead who was in charge of the Folkestone signal post died. He had been ill for some time and had spent the last four months of his life confined to his bed. It is perhaps not surprising that as a result supervision at the station had been very lax. Lieutenant Bradley from the nearby Naval Rendezvous, (base for the Press Gang) wrote to Evan Nepean at the Admiralty to report the death and confirm that he had taken the signal codes into safe custody. He was clearly appalled by the state of affairs he had found at the signal station and very critical about the competence of the men on duty there. He said that the midshipman was good at distinguishing most vessels from those of the enemy, but he could neither read nor write and was not to be trusted with making correct signals. A seaman, George Read, he described as being totally unqualified for his job because although he was able to tell a sloop from a brig he was known in the neighbourhood as a bad character. Lieutenant Bradley said he was surprised that Read's employment at the post had lasted for so long. Apparently he had been given the job on the recommendation of his family, but was suspected of stealing coals and candles from the signal hut for his own use. Diplomatically Lieutenant Bradley wrote that he was sure the deceased officer would have put matters right had he been in better health before he died. George Read protested about the report but was dismissed from the service.[13]

Further along the coast at a signal station on top of Beachy Head, Lieutenant Lee was given a minor reprimand for trying to employ his son. The boy was aged six or seven and the Admiralty were clearly perturbed that the lieutenant had interpreted his instructions: **to engage two trusty men** in this way. After some deliberation Lieutenant Lee was informed that making an application to employ his son was improper, but that on this occasion his misdemeanour would be overlooked.[14]

At the end of 1804 following one of his periodic inspections of the coast stations Admiral Berkley voiced criticism of Lieutenant Edge who was in charge of the post on the tip of Selsey Bill in Sussex. In his report he said that because of the dangerous rocks and shoals of the Owers which was the site of many ship wrecks this station was of great importance. The officer in charge here also had other special duties. These included assisting naval and other vessels which got into trouble on the Owers and acting as an agent for Trinty House by passing on information about ships passing the Bill. He recommended that such was the responsibilities of this station that it should have an officer of character and reliability. As the captain in charge of the district had also reported unfavourably on Lieutenant Edge who he said had many defects the Admiralty acted quickly and he was replaced in May by Lieutenant Allen.[15]

There were of course other less serious matters affecting the daily life of the stations on the South Coast all of which were painstakingly reported upon for resolution by senior Admiralty staff officers. At Folkestone Cliff in 1799 Lieutenant Todman arrived to take up duty, but Lieutenant Holdfield who was there refused to leave until the local captain of the Sea Fencibles told him to do so.[16] The opposite happened at Seaford a few years later when Lieutenant Gardiner refused to hand over control to Lieutenant Lucas until he showed him his letter of appointment. The Admiralty commended Lieutenant Gardiner's action and told him to stay there until his replacement let him see it.[17] At one Kent signal post Lieutenant Norwood complained that he had been ordered to attend for duty with the Sea Fencibles. The Admiralty replied promptly instructing Captain Middleton not to give orders which would interfere with the duties of an officer in charge of a signal station.[18] On the Isle of Wight Captain Barton was asked to investigate the circumstances in which an anonymous letter had been received accusing the officer in charge of the Parkhurst station of negligence. The captain made his enquiries and reported back to the Admiralty that the letter was malicious and untrue.[19]

The coast signal service was not popular with ships at sea and there were occasions when its actions upset senior and influential members of the establishment. In such circumstances the Admiralty acted as arbitrator and tried to placate sensitive feelings on both sides. An examination of the correspondence suggests they did so with fairness. At Folkestone, Lieutenant Halstead before he became ill, reported that he had asked the mayor to fire the guns of the town battery to warn merchant ships in the offing to the presence of a French privateer. He said there was no time to act otherwise, but in doing so he upset General Greenfield who commanded the local artillery in the area. Lieutenant Halstead then caused further discord by refusing to let the General see his orders about his duties and limits of responsibility. In their reply the Admiralty told Lieutenant Halstead that although they agreed he had acted from the best of intentions he should have consulted General Greenfield before giving orders to the battery and also let him see his orders.[20]

The co-operation which was necessary between naval ships offshore and the signal posts was frequently marred by distrust and sometimes outright hostility. This came about because ships passing signal posts were expected to respond to their challenge by giving their private number and signal for the day. Sometimes through perversity or lax watch keeping they did not do so causing the shore station to report in their journal that their challenge had been ignored. This in turn led to the Admiralty to ask the Admiral responsible to explain or rebuke the ship thought to have been at fault. Understandably naval ships on war station at sea resented being burdened with such incidents being brought to the attention of their senior commanders by a lowly lieutenant ashore, especially when a reprimand followed. The tension between the two branches of the service shows in an exchange of correspondence when Admiral Montague, commanding in the Downs, took umbrage because the officer at the Little Cornhill post near Dover was dining out when he sent for him to make a signal. When asked to apologise the lieutenant said he had committed no crime, but he wrote later to say he had intended no disrespect and wished to apologise for any inconveniece he had caused. This did not satisfy Admiral Montague who was out for blood and he asked for punitive action to be taken. The Admiralty replied curtly telling him that an apology had been made and he should accept it.[21] Signallers living on lonely headlands, unarmed and defenceless, were at risk of attack from smuggling gangs and French prisoners of war who had escaped and were trying to return to France. Such men were a particular menace in Kent and East Sussex. At the East Hill station near St Margaret's at Cliffe Lieutenant Turner asked in 1796 for a musket and brace of pistols to protect his men. So seriously was the threat taken that the Admiral in charge of naval squadrons in the Downs was asked to issue the weapons.[22] At Fairlight near Hastings, Lieutenant Gardner was accosted by an angry mob because he had signalled their presence to the Customs and their smuggled cargo of tubs of wines and spirits had been captured.[23] At the Dunnose signal station on the Isle of Wight, Lieutenant Codd complained that being 3 miles (5km) from his nearest neighbour he was concerned in case he might be attacked or 'interrupted' as he put it. His demand was for a swivel cannon, muskets, pistols and two cutlasses. Lieutenant Todman at Folkestone Cliff had a different and unusual problem. It seems that John Holdfield who had been a former midshipman at the station had become the owner of a public house nearby. Presumably, to improve his profits he had been found lighting fires at night as a warning to smugglers of the presence of the Coastguard. The Admiralty, uncertain as to what action to take consulted their legal experts, but it seems their advice was inconclusive, or perhaps the local magistrates were unco-operative, for they were told that Mr Holdfield had done nothing to forfeit his licence.[24]

Life at the signal posts seems to have been mainly a mixture of tedium and frustration and was probably just as uncomfortable as that aboard ships on blockade duty in the Channel. Lieutenant John Gardner, who was later to be promoted commander, left an account of the time he spent at the Fairlight post from 1806 until he was told to shut it down eight years later when he received that 'affectionate farewell' letter from the Admiralty quoted at the start of this chapter.[25] It was an important post because merchant and smaller coastal vessels sailed across Rye Bay an area where privateers made unexpected attacks from the shelter of the French coast. He says he got no respite from watching out for the enemy and also from reporting on the movements of smugglers and escaped prisoners of war. His only relief came when thick fog descended and this sometimes lasted for nine or ten days. He made use of this break to go for walks around the cliffs and along the shore. His job was a frustrating one, for he tells of how when the wind blew from the west the navy guard ships in the Channel sailed into the protection of the eastern shores of the Dungeness Peninsular. It was then that the French privateers seized their opportunity and swooped down to pick off merchant vessels before the guard ships could return. He continues: **I have heard many say that a signal station was an easy berth, and only fit for old and worn-out officers. This I flatly deny; and, without fear of contradiction, can safely say that I suffered more from anxiety at this station than ever I did on board a man of war. In the latter, when one's watch is over, a little rest could be obtained; but at the station the night was worse than the day as the (French invasion) flotilla were expected to take advantage of the darkness so as to be over in the morning, and the night signal was more anxiously watched than that of the day. When Earl St Vincent was first Lord of the Admiralty, Lieutenant John Page (an old school fellow) applied to him for a signal station stating that he was unfit for active service in consequence of a paralytic stroke which affected his arm and one eye. His Lordship wrote for answer, 'That an officer of a signal station ought to have two eyes, and dammed good eyes they ought to be.' However, he gave him the job.**

Lieutenant Gardner's post at Fairlight stood on a gorse studded headland high above the sea where strong winds and southerly gales were common at any season of the year. Because of its construction the signal house took a lot of punishment in bad weather and Lieutenant Gardner says that he continually worried it would not survive. About one storm he writes: **I'm astonished that the house did not blow away. I well remember one dreadful gale blowing down our chimney which lay upon the roof without breaking through, forming an angle of 45° and the midshipman crawling out on all fours (for we could not stand upright), declared he thought it was our 18 pounder carronade that was blown there and had taken that position for a long shot. The fire blew out of the stoves, and the glass out of the window frames; the night was as black as Erebus, with heavy rain which formed a river that swept everything before it; the chief part of our garden washed or blown away, leaving nothing but the bare rock behind, so I wished myself in the old Bay of Biscay again.**

Despite the harsh demands of his command Lieutenant Gardner seems to have managed to enjoy an active social life associating with ordinary and professional people in the area. He says that he kept on good terms with everyone from mayor to fisherman and counted the local clergy as personal friends. One of these was the Reverend Richard Wadeson, vicar of Fairlight, who came to the post frequently to play backgammon although he was said to be a poor loser. Another was the vicar of Hastings, the Reverend Webster Whistler who was known for preaching a powerful sermon. He invited the lieutenant into his home and often gave him presents of fruit and game.

Food and other provisions for the signal post were bought in Hastings and these were fetched by one of the sailors who used to travel to market with a raven he had tamed perched on his shoulder.

In summer the views of the countryside from the top of Fairlight made it a popular place for visitors from far and wide to visit and picnic. Horse coaches brought Cockneys for a day out, but visitors were regarded as a nuisance because they trespassed over the signal site asking ridiculous questions of the seamen. Life in the signal stations was different, but given companionable officers and men it was possibly freer and much safer than in a cramped naval ship at sea.

Letter of Appointment to
Signal Station Lieutenants

*William Marsden, Secretary to the Admiralty wrote personally on behalf of their Lordships to each Lieutenant appointed to the command of a signal post explaining his responsibilities and duties. A copy of the letter sent to Lieutenant John Rodgers at Hawk Hill, (Whitehawk, Brighton) on 15th February 1804 is reproduced here with the original spelling.*

*By the Commiffioners for Executing the Office
of Lord High Admiral of the United
Kingdom of Great Britain
and Ireland Etc.*

*WHEREAS We have caufed Signal Pofts to be erected at the feveral Stations or Places mentioned in the inclofed Lifts for the purpofe of conveying to the Commanding Officers at the feveral Ports, and to His Majefty's Ships and Veffels, Information of fuch of the Enemy's Ships and Vessels, Information of fuch of the Enemy's Ships as may be difcovered from any of the faid Stations; And whereas we intend that you fhall have the charge and direction of making signals from the Station at Hawkhill as well as to repeat thofe made from other Stations; you are hereby required and directed to repair thither, without lofs of time, and take upon you the Charge and Direction of making and repeating Signals accordingly, conformable to the Scheme herewith delivered to you.*

*For the better enabling you to perform this Service, you are to engage one intelligent Petty Officer, and two trufty Men to affift you therein (if not already procured) and, to the end that it may be punctually and effectually executed, you are not upon any pretence whatfoever to be abfent from your Station without our Permiffion, nor are you to fuffer above one of the Persons appointed to affift you to be abfent at the fame time, nor is the time of fuch abfence to exceed 24 hours.*

*You will find upon your arrival at the Station a Temporary Building or Signal Houfe, confifting of two Rooms, with neceffary Furniture, viz. One for the accommodation of yourfelf, the other for your affiftants, which you are to take into your charge; as alfo a Telefcope, one Red Flag, one Blue Pendant, and four Signal Balls; the Colours and Balls to be houfed, and the Yard fecured up and down the the Signal Staff, when they are not in ufe.*

*You are to confider the great object of eftablifhing thefe Pofts, is, that no Ship or Veffel of the Enemy fhall be able to approach the Coaft without being difcovered to be fuch from one of the Pofts; and you are therefore, upon difcovering any of the Enemy's Ships or Cruizers, inftantly to make it known by fhewing the Signal for that purpofe, or repeating it if made by others; and as the Signals are appointed to denote the principal Stations along the Coaft, you will be careful to make the Signal for the Principal Station from whence the Enemy were firft feen (or where the Signal originated) immediately after the firft Signal has been repeated by the next Signal Staff to you, in order that the Commanding Officers at the different Ports, and His Majefty's Ships and Veffels may be informed at what part of the Coaft the Enemy are likely to be met with and intercepted; and in cafe a Signal originates at any of the intermediate Stations (not numbered, or reckoned as a principal one) the Signal denoting the neareft principal Station to fuch intermediate one is to be flewn in the manner above directed.*

*When you difcover any Ship or Ships of War upon the Coaft, fufficiently near for them to difcern Signals, you are to demand by the signal for that purpofe, fuch Ship or Ships to fhew the Private Signal for the day; and if fhe or they fail to do fo in a reafonable time, you are to give notice thereof to the next Station by fignifying, either that fhe is an Enemy, that you are doubtful, or fuch other Information as circumftances require, and the Scheme of Signals affords; and you will always regard the appearance of Ships of War upon the Coaft as an object worthy of the Notice of the neareft Commanding Officer, if fuch Ships do not difcover themfelves to belong to His Majefty, by fhewing the Private signal.*

You will receive herewith a Copy of the Private Signals which are to be delivered to the Kings Ships, by which they are to make themselves known to the different Signal Posts; and you are most strictly enjoined and commanded not to communicate them to any person whatever, except to such Officers as may be sent to relieve you by us, but to keep them carefully concealed, that the Enemy may not come to the knowledge of them.

If you shall at any time discover a Body of the Enemy's Forces landing, or attempting to land, upon any part of the Coast, if it is day-light, you are to make it known by the proper Signal, by Expresses, and by every other means in your power; and if it happens to be in the night, or too dark for Signals to be distinguished, you are to kindle a large Fire at your Post, fire Guns, and make such Intelligence known by every method you can devise.

You are to keep a Journal, in which is to be inserted all Signals made and repeated at your Station, the day and hour when hoisted, and how long kept flying; with such remarkable Occurrences as may be deemed worthy of our Notice, that it may be ascertained (in Case of any Negligence) at which Station it arose; a fair Copy of which Journal is to be sent Weekly to our Secretary, so as to arrive at this Office on a Wednesday.

You are to cause a very strict look out to be kept from your Station, not only upon Vessels that may be in sight, but also upon the Signal Posts to the Eastward and Westward of you, that no time may be lost in communicating to the other Stations Intelligence respecting the Enemy, or other material Information.

And as his Majesty's Ships will occasionally desire to know from you whether you have seen or heard of the Enemy upon the Coast, you are to pay the strictest regard to the mode prescribed for this purpose in the Private Signals before-mentioned, and to give the Ships demanding such Intelligence every Information in your power.

You will be particularly careful to inform all Trading Vessels by the Signals No 9, 10 and 11, as circumstances may require, when it is known that any of the Enemy's Cruizers are upon the Coast, and there is a probability that such trading Vessels may meet with them from the Course they are steering.

And for your Care and Trouble in performing this Service you will be allowed Five Shillings a day and Three Shillings Subsistence, the Petty Officers employed under you the Pay of Midshipmen of a 4th rate, with Two Shillings a day Subsistence; and the two Men Two Shillings per Diem each, the same to be paid Weekly, the Navy Board being directed to imprest to you in the first instance Thirty Pounds, and from time to time upon application to them such further Sums as may be necessary for that purpose; an account of which Payments, with proper Vouchers, are to be transmitted to the said Board at the expiration of every Month towards clearing you of the said Imprest.

Given under Our Hands the 15 day of February 1804.

To: Lieut. John Rodgers
Hawkhill

T. Troubridge
Jas Adams
J. Lemon

By Command of their Lordships
William Marsden

Source PRO ADM 49/110

| Month and Days | Time of making Signals | Wind | Remark |
|---|---|---|---|
| June Wednesday 21ˢᵗ | No Signal made | Easterly | Fine fair Weather. A Brigg of War sailed from Dover road |
| Thursday dº 22ᵈ | At 7 Evening made the Signal Nº 16, seeing a French Lugger in with the French land. a Sloop of War in the Offing. |  |  |
| Friday dº 23ᵈ | No Signal made | SWº | Strong Gail with rain. Dº in the offing. |
| Saturday dº 24ᵗʰ | dº | dº | Dº Wᵉʳ Dº in the Offing |
| Sunday dº 25ᵗʰ | dº | Lº | fine fair Wᵉʳ Dº dº |
| Monday dº 26ᵗʰ | At 3½ past Noon made the Signal Nº 16. a large Lugger in with the French land, a Brigg of War sailed from dº | Dº Wᵉʳ 2 Briggs of War at anchor in Dover road |
| Tuesday dº 27ᵗʰ | No Signal made | Easterly | Dº Wᵉʳ A Convoy passed from the Downs and a Convoy from the Westward turning to Windward. |

*Weekly return of proceedings at the Signal post little corn hill near Dover.*

Signal post little corn hill near Dover 27ᵗʰ June 1797. A Brown Lieut

**15. The journal for Little Corn Hill signal post near Dover, written up by Lieutenant A. Brown and recording his activity for one week 21st - 27th June 1797.**

**16. The Post Captain**

*A senior naval captain, sometimes of post rank, but no longer employed at sea was put in charge of the signal posts and Sea Fencible force in each coastal district.*

---

**PRIVATE SIGNALS,** *by which HIS MAJESTY'S SHIPS are to be made known to the different SIGNAL POSTS established along the Coast.*

| WEEK DAYS. | To be made with Flags, where best seen |
|---|---|
| Monday | Blue pierced White |
| Tuesday | Yellow Red Yellow |
| Wednesday | White and Red |
| Thursday | Dutch |
| Friday | Union |
| Saturday | Blue and Yellow |
| Sunday | Blue |

*NB. These SIGNALS to be in force for the Civil Day beginning at Midnight.*

---

*A SIGNAL to be occasionally made from* **HIS MAJESTY'S SHIPS,** *to the Principal* **SIGNAL POSTS,** but not until after the **PRIVATE SIGNAL** *for the Day has been first shewn by such Ships and answered by the* **SIGNAL POST.**

| SIGNAL. | Place where. | SIGNIFICATION. |
|---|---|---|
| Yellow Flag | Main Topmast or Top gallant Mast head? | Have you seen or heard of the Enemy upon the Coast? |

*NB. Should this SIGNAL be answered in the Affirmative, you are then to shew the PRIVATE SIGNAL for the following Day. the SIGNAL POST will immediately after display the SIGNAL for the Station, from whence the Enemy were last seen, or standing towards.*

**17. 'Most Secret' Private Signals**

*Admirals at sea were issued with printed proformas to be completed by hand with the signals to be used for communication between their ships and the signal posts on shore. Private Signals were necessary to confirm the authenticity of a friendly British warship. The Admiral could change the signals at any time.*

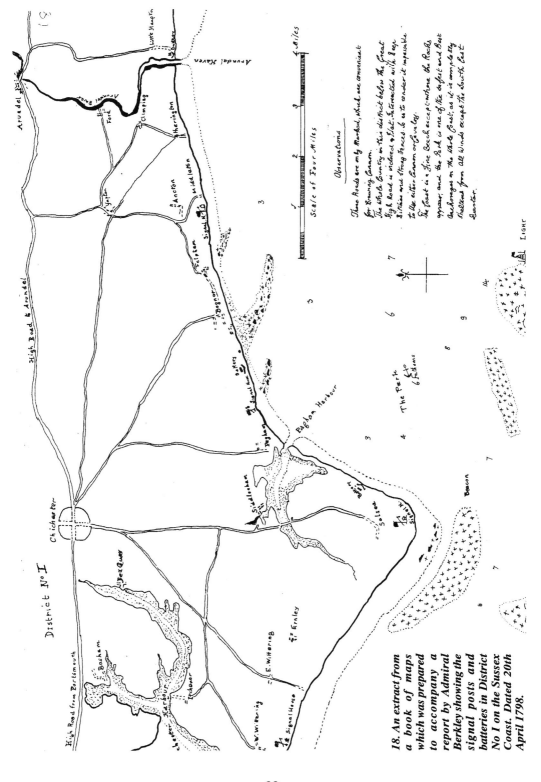

18. An extract from a book of maps which was prepared to accompany a report by Admiral Berkley showing the signal posts and batteries in District No I on the Sussex Coast. Dated 20th April 1798.

# CHAPTER 5

# Flying the Flags

**The King's ships are to make themselves known as they pass the signal posts on the coast, by hoisting an union jack over the signal, expressive of the numbers opposite to their names on the list of the navy.[1]**

The main duties of the lieutenant in each signal station were to monitor the passage of ships along the coast; challenge those ships of war he was doubtful about by using the Private Signal Code and reporting their movements to adjacent posts and naval vessels in the Channel. He also had to repeat and pass on the signals flown from nearby stations. From time to time he might receive signal communications from cruisers, and these and any other incident of importance would have to be reported to his superior the Sea Fencible captain in charge of the district. This officer was usually based at the nearest port or naval harbour. Thus signalling went on between stations along the coast and to and from ships up to 20 miles (32km) out at sea. Once a post in the line began to signal it was repeated and acknowledged by others east and west of the station which originated the first signal. The Admiralty did set some limits on the distance a message travelled, but these were usually decided by the Sea Fencible captains. For example, signals originating between Land's End and Plymouth were not repeated further east than Plymouth. Signals from stations between Plymouth and the Isle of Wight were not repeated further east and west of these places respectively. There was no limitation when the incident was regarded as 'extraordinary', which meant when there were signs of an invasion or an enemy fleet movement of importance. If these occurred, no limits applied.[2] From the way in which the instructions were worded, messages which began at signal posts on the South Coast were passed to all stations between the North Foreland and the Needles. Of the 26 stations along this stretch of the coast, eleven were designated 'Principal' posts which gives an idea of the area's importance because there were only 40 between Land's End and Edinburgh. 'Principal' posts served as reference points on Admiralty charts from which the sailing course of the enemy was taken.[3] Each 'Principal' post had its own unique flag signal, and all stations and captains of naval vessels had a list of these and their locations on the coast.[4] The remaining 15 South Coast stations were known as 'Intermediate' posts. There might be several or none of these between each 'Principal' station depending on the topography of the coastline and its strategic importance to the usual shipping lanes. The sites of many 'Principal' posts were well known landmarks to experienced mariners and included Dungeness Point (Kent), Beachy Head (Sussex), and Ashey Down and the Needles on the Isle of Wight. The 'Intermediate' posts had no flag of identification. When they originated a message they followed it with the flag signal for the nearest 'Principal' station.

Before they opened for business each signal post was issued with a newly devised code of set message signals solely for the purpose of communicating with each other and naval ships at sea. Most naval ships were also given a copy so they could reply to, or make signals to the shore. As a security measure the code was produced in two parts, the enemy needing to capture both to make sense of either.[5] The first part entitled, 'Signals to be made at the Several Signal Posts along the Coast' showed flags, balls and pennants in different positions each combination being numbered. The second was an explanation with the title, 'Signification of Signals to be made at the Several Signal Posts along the Coast' and it gave the meaning of each signal. The following is an example from both parts,

Signal Number 58
Meaning - The Enemy's fleet is at sea

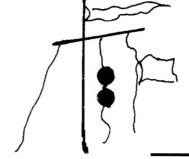

The first list of signals for signal posts had about 92 different signals, but as the long war with France continued, changes and additions were made and between 1807 and 1810 this number was increased to 119.[6] Nearly half the signals were about the kind of vessel seen: frigates, transports, or privateers, and the actual or anticipated movement of warships from the French coast. A series of signals, numbered 40-50 were used to warn that French squadrons were about to leave, or had sailed, from the embarkation ports of Texel, Flushing, Ostend, Dunkirk, Calais, Dieppe, Havre, Cherbourg and Boulogne. Five signals numbered 55-59 were about enemy ship movements from Brest, another embarkation port for an invasion of Britain.

The actual landing of a French army on the South Coast was covered by signals giving orders and instructions to the Sea Fencibles and defending troops. The list was added to as time passed to give orders about the new and growing menace from privateers, smugglers, and escaped prisoners of war. There were also procedural signals about the mechanics of message sending, and the confirmation, enquiry and cancellation of transmissions. In 1809 and 1810 the Admiralty filled in further spare spaces in the signal code. Signals 114-119 were about convoy sailings and their protection where more than five merchantmen had scattered. There was also a special block of signals numbers 23 to 25 and 38 and 54 which gave orders to British squadrons searching for French ships trying to escape the blockade off the French, Belgium, and Dutch coasts. These signals were only to be used by signal stations between the Humber and the sea area of the Downs off the Kent coast.

During the summer of 1803 when an invasion was expected almost daily, the Admiralty sent to the generals commanding troops on the South Coast certain additional signals. These included numbers 40-50 which gave information about the French leaving their embarkation ports, and the direction in which their troop transports were sailing.

In places where there was an important military headquarters with many regiments standing on guard behind earthworks put up to defend the coast, flagstaffs were manned by soldiers to receive these signals direct from the Channel squadrons. One of these was at Shorncliffe near Hythe. Such flagstaffs supplemented the work of the naval signal stations, but were under military control.

Possibly because of the extra vulnerability of the South Coast, Admirals commanding the seas were given seventeen special day and night signals about different invasion possibilities. As the Admiralty explained in its instructions: **(we think) it proper to make some addition to the signals to be used at the different signal stations on the coast for the better information of H.M. ships, Commanding Officers of H.M. troops on shore, in the event of any attempt being made by the enemy to invade this country...** Ten of these signals said that the enemy squadrons were about to leave, or had already left embarkation ports between Texel and and Boulogne. Each signal referred to a different port. The next three signals said that the French were already on the coast, were warships, transports or gun boats. The final four signals were about expected enemy landings to the east or west, or about landings already having taken place.[7]

The Admiralty was well aware of the difficulty of keeping the various signal codes secret at the signal posts and on ships. But its instructions for 'Private' signals were regarded by many senior naval officers as impractical. When Lord Keith received an order telling him not to send the new signals to officers below the rank of commander, he replied that he had already done so because the lieutenants in charge of his armed cutters had already got them. He said that previous orders had told him to issue the signal codes to all naval vessels and this is what he had done, otherwise how would they have been able to reply to the challenge made by the signal stations. Sir James Colboys who commanded in Plymouth made a similar submission. It seems that confusion arose because the Admiralty had not realised that so many small naval craft were being used to patrol the seas immediately off the coast. Understandably with so many copies of the signal codes in circulation the Admiralty were worried, particularly in case the 'Private' signals were captured. Eventually the issue was resolved by a decision to give the 'Private' signals' only to vessels listed in the 'Signal Book for Ships of War'. In respect of the many hundreds of smaller craft Admirals were invited to: **make suggestions by which such craft should make themselves known to signal posts and thereby prevent alarm by being mistaken for privateers.**[8] They did so and the smaller craft were issued with a different set of 'Private' signals so that if these were captured the signal codes for the larger ships were not compromised.

The 'Private' signals were really passwords in that they were combinations of numbers, made as secure as possible by changing the sequence daily, weekly or at some other frequency. Between signal stations and warships 'Private' signals were used to confirm the identity of vessels as friendly if there was any doubt on this point. The password combinations of numbers were worked out in the Admiralty Office and one copy was sent to each Admiral with a supply of blank forms which he was told to fill in with the new signals for distribution to each of his captains. A copy was also sent by express service in the mail coach to each signal station.

Signals were changed when ships were captured or lost in circumstances which suggested they had not been destroyed, or when news was received of the codes being compromised.[9] During the July of 1810 the Admiralty got reports that this had happened to the 'Private' signals used by some naval brigs and luggers in the English Channel and steps were taken to replace these with new ones from 1st September.[10] As this shows, changing signal codes was a lengthy and expensive business.

The publication 'Signal Book for Ships of War' was a list of all British warships giving their name and identity number. It was kept in the personal possession of the commander and when his ship passed a signal post or entered port he was required to hoist flags to make his number. Disputes over whether this procedure was properly carried out were not uncommon and it was usual for the Admiralty to call for reports from both parties to explain their side of the case. In 1804 Lieutenant Hutchinson on duty at the Dungeness signal post reported that in answer to his signal number 28: **name of the ship is required** a vessel sailing towards Folkestone responded with number 273 which did not appear in the signal book. After an enquiry it was found that the lieutenant had not received an amendment to the list issued by the Admiralty.[11] A more serious incident occurred at Lympne when Lieutenant John found that a French warship was flying the 'Private' signal of the day. The Admiralty arranged for the code to be changed without delay.[12]

From a study of the signalling instructions and entries in the station journals it is possible to reconstruct how the system worked and the use to which it was often put. For example let us suppose that the officer in charge of the Middleton station near Bognor spots a frigate 6 miles (10km) off shore travelling east and acting suspiciously. He challenges by hoisting number 20 which means: **The Private Signal is required from ships of war,** which is ignored. This confirms his doubts and he flies (for the information of nearby signal posts) signal number 19: **neutral ship of war, or it is doubtful if they are friends or enemies.** The lieutenant at the Kingston post 7 miles (11km) to the east of Middleton sees the signal and replies with number 19 acknowledging the message. Another signal station at Pagham 6 miles (10km) to the west takes the same action. The Middleton post noting that the message has been read, hoists the special flag signal denoting the nearest 'Principal'signal station which is the one on Selsey Point. This in turn is acknowledged by the other two stations repeating it. Both signals are then passed and repeated further east and west to other stations. The action likely to follow this exchange of signalling would depend on the naval situation at the time in the area. Guardships off Newhaven and Portsmouth might be expected to see the signal flying from several shore stations and sail to intercept. Keen lookouts on larger warships patrolling in the Channel perhaps 20 miles (32Km) from the coast would be alerted to give chase to intercept. The lieutenant at the Selsey Point station would already have sent a seaman to the battery nearby where men would stand to the 36 pounder guns and be ready to fire if the suspect ship came closer inshore. The message transmitted up and down the coast would eventually reach the naval officer in charge at Portsmouth and Newhaven who could inform the regular military, and turn out the Sea Fencibles if a raid on the shore seemed likely.

A letter in the Times newspaper gives a short but interesting account of joint action by the signal posts and naval frigates in 1804. About 6pm on a light evening in May, a large French flotilla of over one hundred vessels were reported as having left Boulogne. The Folkestone signal station signalled the news and neighbouring posts from Lympne to Dungeness repeated it. The signals were seen by British warships on blockade duty sheltering in the bay east of Dungeness Point and they quickly got underway in the direction of the enemy force.[13]

A crucial factor in judging the effectiveness of the Admiralty coast signal system was how long it took for messages to be passed and acknowledged. Much depended on variable factors such as weather, visibility and the alertness of lookouts who spent long hours with nothing much to do. If these two conditions came right it was a speedy way of passing short basic details over long distances, much quicker than using messengers or boats. However, it is difficult to work out reliable average timings because only a few of the signal journals have survived and those that have, give inconclusive results. From the journals seen the time it took to pass messages between stations varied from five minutes to more than an hour. Some of the longer times resulted from a regulation that a signal had to be kept hoisted until it was seen to be repeated by the next station. No criticism was seen in the Admiralty records about the time taken to transmit signals, although this was sometimes implied in complaints about poor observation by the seamen. Inspecting officers found bad visibility a continual problem, even during the summer months. They were also concerned about seamen who were illiterate and lacking in those qualities needed for a good signalman.

The journals reported on the weather, ships seen from the station, and the time signals were made and acknowledged. Some contained a wealth of detail about weather conditions and the actions of ships seen, but others were skimpy and so generally uninformative leaving an impression of how boring it was to watch an empty sea. The journals were sent weekly to the Admiralty until 1808 when the Sea Fencible captains were asked to look at them first and make comments.[14] After 1812 those signal posts which were a long way (over 3 miles (5km)) from a post office were allowed to send their journals fortnightly in summer and monthly during the winter.[15] The Admiralty took completion of these records very seriously and told the lieutenant of a post at Sheerness that his blank report was not satisfactory because even if no signals had been hoisted the variations in the weather should have been reported.[16]

The uneasy relations which occasionally existed between ship's captains and signal station lieutenants have already been mentioned. These arose from the neglect of watch keepers to reply to signal number 28 **The name of the ship or vessel passing is required**.[17] Inevitably failure to respond to the challenge led to senior officers on both sides defending their men. Thus Captain Owen in Walmer Roads rebuffed complaints made by two adjacent signal posts at Hawk Hill (Brighton) and Shoreham saying in explanation: **I know from the ships of the bay plying up and down the Channel do often omit answering the signals made at the signal post, but I am positive that no general charge of this nature can be made against the areas under me, and attention to signals is a strong article in the instructions.** Then moving on to the attack he counterclaims by referring to an action off Seaford when a French lugger got away and says: **the circumstances seem not to have been observed by the gentlemen at the post who reported their complaint to the Admiralty, and I thought it my duty to tell Lord Keith that they are incompetent judges of the conduct of cruisers.**[18]

The Admiralty found that the wrong use of signals was as much a nuisance to the efficiency of the system as was the neglect to answer them. Admiral Nelson reacted vehemently each time a ship left Boulogne and flew signal number 50:**The enemy squadron appears to be ready or preparing to sail from Boulogne,** to alert other vessels in the vicinity. He implored the Admiralty to change the wording to mean that the French fleet had actually sailed, but was only steering along the French coast. His suggestion to limit its use in this way he thought was essential if his captains were to be neither inattentive to signals nor improperly annoyed by them. In his condemnation of signal number 50 to be regarded as an alarm he said: **that it had no effect on him as he knew from experience that it meant nonsense.** [19]

Either because of misunderstandings or panic by those manning the signal post, false alarms happened from time to time. Two serious incidents occurred in the summer of 1803 when there was much fear of an invasion in the southern counties. Admiral Montague, the Portsmouth naval commander, acted on a signal from Lieutenant Falkener of the Fort Cumberland post and ordered the squadrons anchored at Spithead out to sea. He told the Admiralty later that although the alarm had been raised in what he described as a strange and confused manner, which he thought may have been a mistake, he had decided that the threat of an invasion was so great he could not ignore it. Apparently the enemy force which had been seen was only a single row galley. In another incident also involving Lieutenant Falkener and a wrong signal he claimed he had only repeated the message he had received from another signal post. The Admiralty ordered an enquiry which was carried out by Captain O'Bryan in charge of the Sea Fencibles in the Gosport district. When they got his report they expressed their displeasure with Lieutenant Falkener and asked for him to be dismissed as incompetent. The reports are obscure as to whether this was done and if another post was also involved, which may have been Pagham, but the matter ended in the dismissal of one of the officers. During the course of these enquiries it was suggested in mitigation of the errors that there was no suitable signal which described the number of enemy boats seen. Admiral Montague recommended a new signal to prevent further mistakes, but was told that number 11 **An enemy ship or vessel close under land** was quite sufficient.[20]

Because the Admiralty were so worried about the confusion and cost of false alarms they acted with severity towards those found to be responsible. However, mistakes occurred in all areas and were usually the result of human error of one kind or another. Captain Shield in the Harwich district was ordered to investigate when one of his stations displayed signal number 40 which meant that the French squadrons were preparing to leave the Texel off Northern Holland.[21] A curious event also happened on the Kent coast early in September 1803 which gives some idea of the upset and panic a false alarm caused. The Folkestone signal post hoisted number 42 **Enemy squadron appears to be ready or preparing to sail from Ostend.** As the weather was good with a fresh wind blowing it was anticipated that an attack could come within a few hours. The troops were alerted and the volunteers and Sea Fencibles called to arms. The men are said to have assembled with cheerfulness and great alacrity. In the midst of the emergency the Mayor of Hythe took umbridge when his waggons and horses were confiscated by Lieutenant Colonel Hawker for the movement of troops. It seems that with much abuse he refused to part with his horses until a formal warrant for the seizure was given to him. This unseemly obstinate bureaucratic behaviour at such a time of crisis dismayed those who saw it and reports on the episode were sent to the Commander-in-Chief. [22]

General Sir John Moore who had been urgently recalled from his inspection of the gun batteries at Dungeness to take command of the troops in the neighbourhood was in no doubt about the seriousness with which this alarm was taken. He wrote later to his mother saying how lucky she was to have left the coast earlier in the day. He explained that the signal post had confused Ostend with Calais and sent the wrong signal.[23]

During the early years of the signal station operations many suggestions were made for extra signals and ideas to improve or clarify the existing ones. There were proposals for signals to pinpoint more precisely the course and position of the ships sighted from the shore, and for all 'Intermediate' posts to be given their own flag signal. As early as 1795 Lieutenant Bray of the Revenue Cutter **Hind** devised a scheme along these lines, and in 1803 Captain Edge of the Suffolk district raised the matter again.[24] But the Admiralty were firm in their opposition to any change and rejected most suggestions. It is clear from their consistent arguments that they had no wish to depart from what was a basic and simple system with a minimum number of signals. In their view the advantages which might be gained by using a more complicated display of flags was likely to be outweighed by an increase in misunderstandings and false alarms. In arriving at this conclusion the Admiralty were undoubtedly influenced by the limitations of some of their officers and signalmen and the hazards of reading other than very simple signal displays to be interpreted correctly over long distances in poor visibility. This concern was certainly justified, especially during the invasion crisis years of 1803-5. False alarms meant that ships and men could be sent off on a wild goose chase in the wrong direction, moves that could cripple the best defence strategy for guarding a long coastline.

As well as being reluctant to make changes in the system of coast signals it was also strict Admiralty policy not to disclose the meaning of the signals outside the naval service. This, despite many requests from the captains of merchant ships, who wanted to know whether they were sailing into the path of the enemy. Eventually the losses caused by attacks of privateers and strong representations from the Secretary of the newly formed, but powerful Lloyds Underwriters led to the Admiralty to agree to signals number 51 and 52 being made available to the merchant service.[25] These signals gave warning of the presence of French frigates and cruisers and were hoisted at the signal stations when merchantmen were in danger. This decision, which was not made until November 1805, unfortunately led to a muddle two years later when the Admiralty changed the meaning of these two signals and confused them with signals 93 and 94 which were similar, but not necessarily relevant to merchantmen. In response to enquires about the mess, new instructions had to be sent to all ships and signal posts to resolve the matter.[26]

At the onset of winter in 1807 the Admiralty agreed to help the Revenue service by using the chain of signal posts to combat smuggling. The Treasury annoyed at the amount of excise duty being avoided, complained about reports they had received that large numbers of vessels had been spotted lying off the coast and unloading their cargoes into smaller craft for transfer to the shore. The Admiralty told the lieutenants at the signal posts that when they suspected this was taking place they should hoist a new signal, number 104: **Smuggling vessels are at a distance from the shore unloading their cargoes into smaller vessels to be taken on shore.** The purpose of this signal was to inform naval patrols in the vicinity and the nearest port authorities so that retaliatory measures could be taken. As an incentive the Treasury agreed to pay a share of the value of any cargoes successfully seized to the men of the signal post who first signalled the information.[27]

Another duty added to the responsibilities of the signal staff was to assist the civil and military authorities in the recapture of escaped prisoners of war. French soldiers who were held captive in camps, on farms and in working parties would travel to the Kent and Sussex coast where they hoped to steal a boat or persuade smugglers to help them get back to France. Admiralty orders were that when the signal stations were alerted to escaped prisoners being in their neighbourhood they were to signal to the next post and to any naval ships in sight. The signal seems not to have been added to the code, but was to consist of hoisting a triangular flag over a pennant, and this was to be followed by the unique code number of the nearest 'Principal' signal station. The station lieutenants were also told to let the local magistrates know and to encourage them to co-operate in the capture and imprisonment of the prisoners.[28] This may not have been easy given the tolerance shown by many communities in Kent and Sussex to smugglers.

Although the Admiralty coast signal system was set up almost overnight and generally well planned for the task it was expected to undertake, human frailty and the weather almost certainly made it less effective in its day to day operations.

**19. How the Admiralty Signal System worked on the South Coast.**

**Shoreham S.P.**
Repeats signal 19 to the post on **HAWK Hill Brighton**, who repeats it eastwards.

**Worthing S.P.**
Displays the signal seen at **Kingston** and repeats it until it sees it hoisted at **the Shoreham S.P.**

**Kingston S.P.**
Acknowledges **Middleton's** signal by repeating it (Sig 19) and expects it to be taken up by **Worthing S.P.**

**Middleton S.P.**
Spots strange ships 6 miles (10km) offshore. Requests their numbers (Sig 19), but gets no reply. Flies Sig 20 to alert adjacent Signal posts.

**Pagham S.P.**
Sees **Middleton's** signals, and repeats them westward to **Selsey S.P**

**Selsey S.P.**
Relays signals westward to **West Wittering S.P.**

**West Wittering S.P.**
Transmits the signals westward across Langstone Harbour to **Fort Cumberland.**

**Fort Cumberland S.P.**
Passes receipt of the flag signal by messenger to the Admiral at Portsmouth Harbour and also repeats it to the **Ashey Down S.P.** on the Isle of Wight.

**How the System worked.**

**Signal 20** : The 'Private' signal (number) is required from ships of war. **If no reply:**

**Signal 19** : Neutral ship of war, or it is doubtful whether they are Friends or Enemies at... **or**

**Signal 9** : An enemy's frigate or Frigates is at ....

**Position** : The unique flag signal for Selsey Point, the nearest Principal Signal Post, followsthe above signals

**Action likely to follow this exchange of signals.**

1 Naval guard ships patrolling the coast inshore would see the signal and could sail to investigate.

2 Larger warships 15 miles (24km) out at sea would also see the signal in good visibility and could change course to investigate.

3 The gun crews at the Selsey and Bognor Rock batteries would be ordered to stand to.

4 On receipt of the signal the Admiral at Portsmouth would have to decide whether to take any further action.

Any action that was taken was neither speedy nor necessarily effective.

miles

0    2·5    5    7·5

45

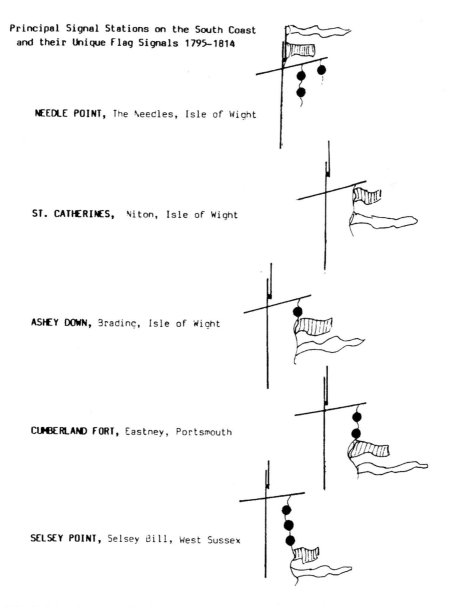

Principal Signal Stations on the South Coast
and their Unique Flag Signals 1795-1814

NEEDLE POINT, The Needles, Isle of Wight

ST. CATHERINES, Niton, Isle of Wight

ASHEY DOWN, Brading, Isle of Wight

CUMBERLAND FORT, Eastney, Portsmouth

SELSEY POINT, Selsey Bill, West Sussex

**20. Principal signal posts stood at fixed points on the shore from which the course of enemy ships was computed and signalled up and down the coast to naval vessels able to intercept them.**

Principal Signal Stations on the South Coast and their Unique Flag Signals 1795-1814

NEEDLE POINT, **The Needles, Isle of Wight**

ST. CATHERINES, *Niton, Isle of Wight*

ASHEY DOWN, **Brading, Isle of Wight**

CUMBERLAND FORT, **Eastney, Portsmouth**

SELSEY POINT, **Selsey Bill, West Sussex**

HAWK HILL, **Whitehawk, Brighton, Sussex**
BEACHY HEAD, **Eastbourne, East Sussex**
DUNGENESS, **Lydd on Sea, Kent**
LITTLE CORNHILL, **South Foreland, Dover**
EAST HILL, **west of Deal, Kent**
NORTH FORELAND, **south of Margate, Kent**

**HAWK HILL,** Whitehawk, Brighton, Sussex

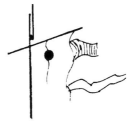

**BEACHY HEAD,** Eastbourne, East Sussex

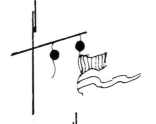

**DUNGENESS,** Lydd on Sea, Kent

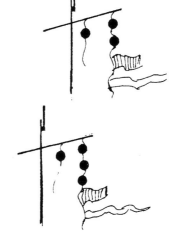

**LITTLE CORNHILL,** South Foreland, Dover

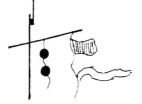

**EAST HILL,** west of Deal, Kent

**NORTH FORELAND,** south of Margate, Kent

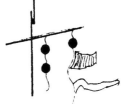

21. An early 19th century map of the Shornecliff camp area near Hythe, Kent, showing the eastern end of the Royal Military Canal and other defences including Martello Tower No 9, the square redoubt which was never armed, and the battery with the military signal post for receiving signals for the general from the navy. Explanations have been added to the map.

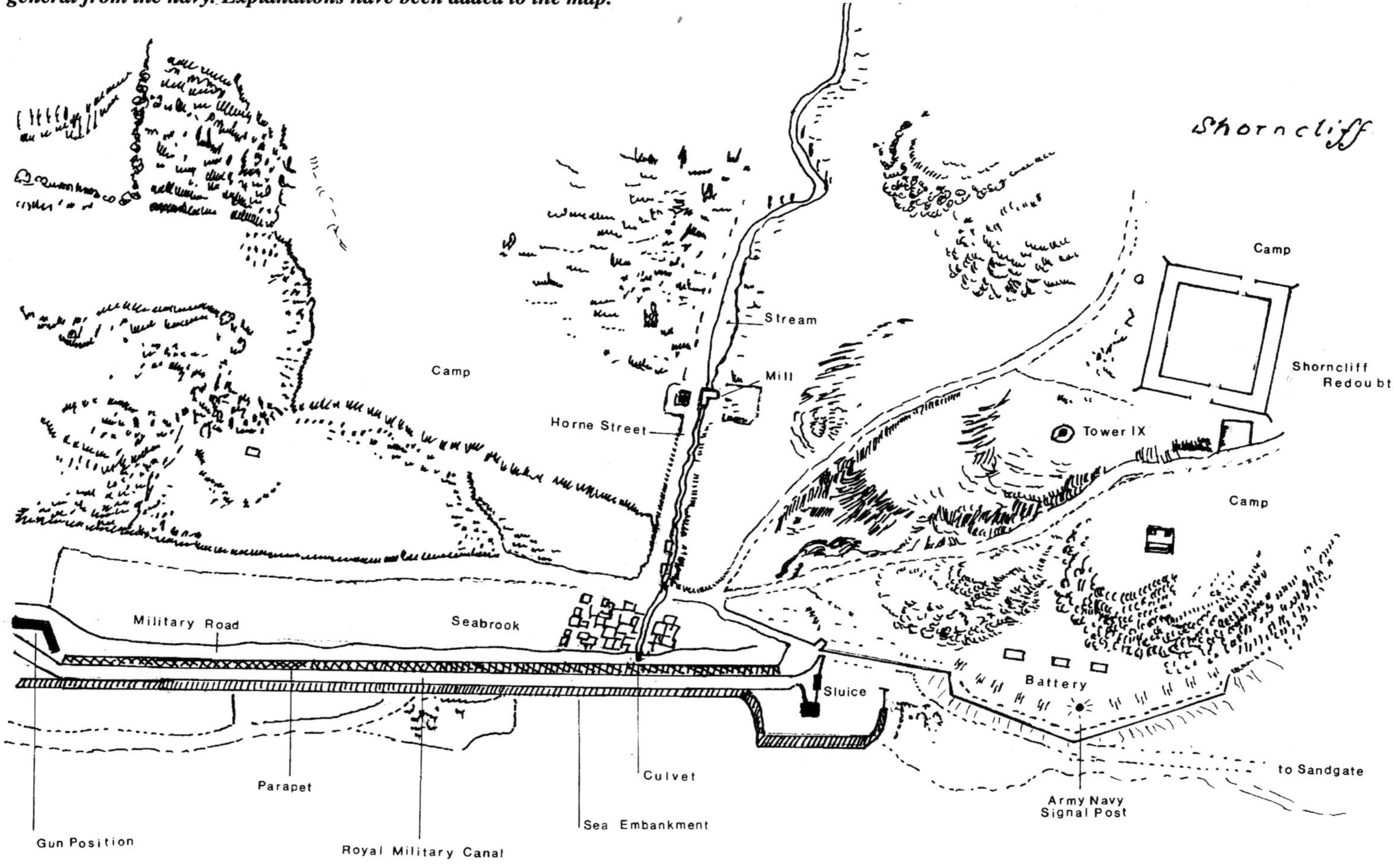

Shorncliff

Camp

Shorncliff Redoubt

Camp

to Sandgate

Tower IX

Battery

Army Navy Signal Post

Stream

Mill

Sluice

Culvet

Sea Embankment

Horne Street

Seabrook

Camp

Royal Military Canal

Parapet

Military Road

Gun Position

*Signal Book for Ships of War 1799*

| | |
|---|---|
| 1028 Delight | Sloop |
| 1029 Linnet | Cutter |
| 1031 Maida | 74 guns |
| 1032 Sleeste | 38 guns |
| 1033 Celebis | 33 guns |
| 1034 Malacca | 36 guns |
| 1035 Sir Edwin Hughes | 38 guns |
| 1036 Cornwallis | 38 guns |
| 1037 Duncan | 74 guns |
| 1038 Psyche | 36 guns |
| 1039 Pitt | 74 guns |
| 1041 Sir Francis Drake | 38 guns |
| 1042 Salsette | 36 guns |
| 1043 Paz | Schooner |
| 1044 Dolores | Schooner |
| 1045 Cossack | 22 guns |
| 1046 Bergere | Sloop |
| 1047 Derwent | Sloop |
| 1048 Surly | Cutter |
| 1049 Trafalgar | 98 guns |
| 1050 Marengo | 74 guns |
| 1051 Pompeii | 74 guns |
| 1052 Scarborough | 74 guns |
| 1053 Gloster | 74 guns |
| 1054 Mulgrave | 74 guns |
| 1055 Berwick | 74 guns |
| 1056 Edinburgh | 74 guns |
| 1057 Dublin | 74 guns |
| 1058 Rodney | 74 guns |
| 1059 Indus | 74 guns |

**22.** *All naval warships and signal posts were supplied with a 'Signal Book for Ships of War'. This was a consecutive list of numbers with the name and type of vessel printed alongside. Changes to the book were made from time to time and the example shown is an additional page issued by the Admiralty on 6th November 1807.*

**23.** *In reply to a challenge from the signal post on shore the captain of the warship Scarbough, 74 guns, confirms his identity by displaying his unique number '1052' in the Signal Book for ships of War. The numeral flags had to be flown beneath the Union Jack.*

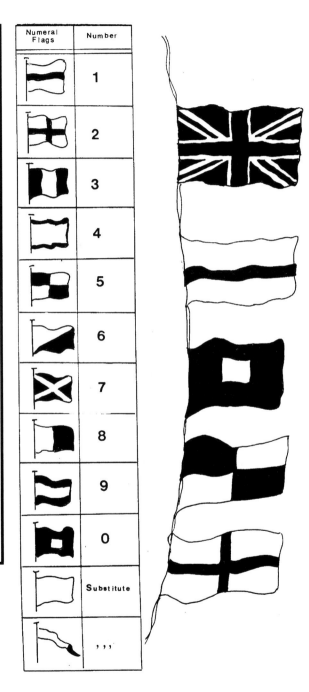

| Numeral Flags | Number |
|---|---|
| | 1 |
| | 2 |
| | 3 |
| | 4 |
| | 5 |
| | 6 |
| | 7 |
| | 8 |
| | 9 |
| | 0 |
| | Substitute |
| | , , , |

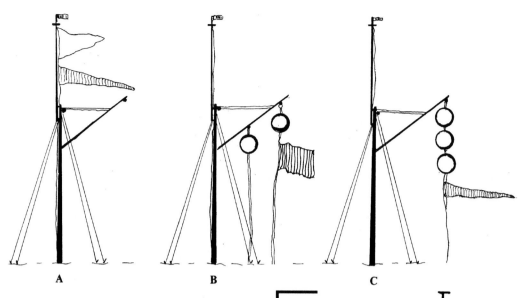

A          B          C

*24. Special Signals used on the Kent and Sussex Coast*

*A Denotes escaped prisoners of war trying to steal a boat to cross to France from the Kent coast.*

*B Signifies smugglers are unloading their cargoes into smaller boats for landing on the beaches.*

*C One of three signals given by the Navy to Lloyds to warn merchant shipping they were in danger because French privateers were at anchor on the English coast.*

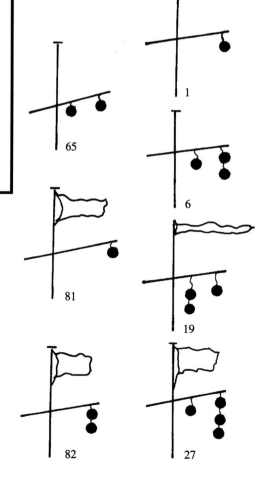

## Examples of other Signals

No 1  The ships of war seen are friends.
No 6  Enemy Transports or Fleet steer west
No 19  Neutral Ship of War or doubtful
        whether they are Friends or Enemies.
No 27  The Channel Fleet is arrived in Torbay
No 65  Sea Fencibles are to embark and the
        boats  to be in readiness to act.
No 81  Enemy are engaged with our troops.
No 82  Enemy are beaten

# CHAPTER 6

# Signals on the Coast at Night

**A chancy and confusing business with
bangs, blue lights and tar barrels.**

*...They stand as signals from the land
Each are a lovely light...*[1]

No one at the Admiralty really thought the French would launch an invasion at night. Such an operation was deemed to be too complex and difficult for the circumstances of the times, and would have been known about in London long before it happened. However, if it was attempted, where the enemy would chose to land his troops was a mystery not to be resolved until the invasion was under way. This question and the possibility of isolated attacks on the coast needed to be tackled given that privateers, gun boats and warships were continually prowling in the Channel. If, however, night skirmishes between French ships and shore stations ever took place there is an absence of reports in the official records to judge their extent and importance.

Many months after the signal posts were set up the Admiralty realized that their instructions about signalling at night from the shore were vague, and left too much to the ingenuity of the officers in charge.[2] It was commonplace for ships at sea to pass limited night signals to each other by using a combination of four lanterns fitted with Muscovy glass and lit by oil. The lamps were displayed in a particular pattern on the ship's mast accompanied by gunfire to draw attention to the signal. In contrast the only guidance given to the signal posts was: **you are to kindle a large fire at your Post, fire guns, and make such intelligence known by every method you can devise.**[3] Advice which was likely to end in confusion instead of positive action, especially as few stations had been given cannon. Concerned about the disruption which would follow from false alarms, perhaps compounded by the use of different night signals on land, the Admiralty asked each station to report on how they interpreted their orders. The replies confirmed its suspicion that no uniform satisfactory arrangements existed and that the station lieutenants were uncertain as to what should be done, given that they had been told not to incur any expense for making signals at night.

Lieutenants J. Turner at East Hill and A. Browne at Little Cornhill in Kent thought that faggots, tar barrels and gunfire would make the best signals although they had made no provision for these to be used at their stations. The officer at Lympne, also in Kent, suggested hoisting tar barrels on high poles, but could make no fires as he had no means of doing so, and complained he did not even possess a lamp.

The best prepared signal post was on Dungeness Point which was adjacent to four gun batteries and a redoubt. Here Lieutenant W. Edger had an agreement with Captain Pole in charge of the redoubt to fire three guns at each of the batteries to alert Hythe Bay to the east and Rye Bay to the west of the point which stretches 6 miles (10km) out to sea. At Fairlight, near Hastings, Lieutenant Chantrell said he could burn gorse faggots of which there were plenty growing on the cliff top, as they still do to this day. If, however, he was to do this he had to compensate the farmer who would charge 70p or 80p for every waggon load. Lieutenant Basden on Seaford Cliff also proposed to make a signal fire of furze faggots and he thought he could buy these from a supplier 3 miles (5km) distance at £1.05 per hundred delivered. Alternatively, he thought he could buy empty tar barrels from 15p apiece from the nearby harbour at Newhaven. Making the most of this opportunity to press the Admiralty for what he wanted, he asked for three cannon to make signals and defend the Cuckmere Valley Haven nearby, which was not his responsibility. He also asked for a boat and a horse for his seamen to use to take messages. At Hawk Hill (Brighton), Lieutenant R.P Shewin had no plans to make night signals, but thought a field gun from the local artillery volunteers would be useful in raising the alarm. Lieutenant Lockhart at Worthing wanted to burn furzes, but Lieutenants Willis at Folkestone Cliff and Lieutenant Brett at Middleton, (Sussex) did not even bother to reply. The officer at West Wittering reckoned he could solve the problem by setting light to a large pile of wood at a safe distance from the signal hut and he also proposed mounting a large lighted lamp at the head of the signal mast. He was anxious to make a signal which would stand out clearly from the fires lit by smugglers on adjacent beaches. This officer also wanted to fire a cannon, but as he only had a musket he doubted whether the shots would be heard at the nearest signal post which was more than 4 miles (6km) away. Lieutenant Taite at Kingston was unhelpful. He said that he had no arrangements for night signalling and could offer no suggestions. The Pagham and Cumberland Fort stations intended to warn nearby coast batteries, and Lieutenant Codd at Dunnose on the Isle of Wight reckoned he could alert half the island in less than a minute if he was given a cannon, and two wagon loads of furzes to make a fire. As the nearest storage shed was 3 miles (5km) distant he was worried about how he was expected to keep the fuel dry.

A summary of the replies received at the Admiralty was neither very informative or innovative although it was evident the majority believed the most effective signal at night would be gunfire, and for this they wanted cannon.[4] Their preference was for either 6 or 18 pounder guns because the noise would distinguish them from the smaller calibre guns used by the smugglers. There were also several requests for horses so that messages could be taken quickly to the nearest military headquarters.

It is perhaps not surprising that neither recommendation was accepted. Cannon were in short supply although a few were issued later on a selective basis to some of the more important signal stations following representations from captains of the the the Sea Fencibles. The Admiralty also made it clear there was no question of the lieutenants incurring extra expenses for horses, fodder and stables, even if there were good reasons for doing so.

After much deliberation the Admiralty eventually approved standard arrangements for raising the alarm at night. It was to be a two part procedure. A pile of furze and tar barrels was to be lit and not until this fire was seen and repeated by the lighting of a similar fire at the next station was the second part of the alarm to be sent.[5] This was to consist of lanterns hoisted in a specific pattern at the top of the signal mast. Inside the lantern blue lights were to be lit. These were bored wooden tubes, or cups with handles, into which was pressed a mixture of saltpetre, sulphur and orpiment covered with cartridge paper. When ignited the substance burnt with a steady reflective blue flame.[6] Night signals did not have quite the same meaning as the day signals and as soon as dawn came the station lieutenant was supposed to hoist a flag signal which was as close as possible to the one sent by lights in the night. It was necessary to do this to ensure that the overnight signal had been correctly received and understood. The inference is that the possibility of a misunderstanding was quite high.

It was of course quite impossible to devise a comprehensive set of signals, similar to those in use in daylight, and to expect them to be transmitted over long distances and be received correctly. Wisely, the Admiralty restricted the number of night signals to five, each one being about the movement of an enemy invasion force. The first signal, corresponding to number 49 for daytime use warned: **The Enemy's ships have put to sea.** The second signal was of greater urgency: **The enemy is approaching towards the coast.** This approximated to a group of day signals numbers 30-37 and 61 which gave the direction the enemy ships were taking. The next two signals were about an actual landing of men on the coast: **Landing to the westward or southward,** and **Landing to the eastward or northward.** The corresponding day signals were numbers 13 and 12 respectively. The fifth signal was an administrative one intended to put right mistakes. It equated with number 18 in the list of day signals and read: **The last signal is no longer to be regarded.**

When ships signalled to the shore at night they used a combination of two, three, or four lights displayed on their masts in a triangular, perpendicular or horizontal pattern. A gun was fired to call attention to the display of lights and it was fired at three or four minute intervals, until an acknowledgement was received from the signal post.[7]

As only a few signal posts had cannon, gunfire did not form part of their signalling procedure with ships. That is why to call attention to the signal they were making, they first had to light a fire. This had to be lit at some distance from the station, partly for safety reasons, but also so that it did not interfere with the blue lights which they hoisted at the top of the mast. The blue lights were burnt in either a horizontal or vertical arrangement, or at laid down intervals of three or four minutes.[8]

Sometimes false fires were used for night signals. These were similar to flares, being bright lights to draw attention to the signal lamps. Traditionally false fires were used to confuse the enemy and although the term is used loosely in naval instructions they were also lit to reinforce other night signals. Night signals of the period are clearly set out in a printed document:

**Signals established between the Cruisers and Commanding Officers of His Majesty's Ships and the Signal Posts; as well as Commanding Officers of His Majesty's troops on Shore.**[9]

Five years after the signal stations were first set up, the Admiralty gave approval for the use of blue lights, furze faggots and tar barrels for night signals at all signal posts. Blue lights were to be ordered from the Board of Ordnance and where supplies were available lieutenants could purchase up to fifty bundles of faggots locally.[10] The furzes had to be piled in a small stack with a narrow ridge at the top with a thatched cover to protect them from bad weather.[11] A request from one station for a shed in which to keep the faggots and a pitchfork for stacking them was rejected. The officer was told to make his own arrangements as the expense could not be met from the public purse.

In 1800 the Admiralty also approved expenditure for fire frames built to a design put forward by Lieutenant

Newall in charge of the Teignmouth post in Devon. The fire frame was a deep basket fashioned from 19mm iron rod and fixed to the top of a standing wooden post 12 feet (3m) high. It held two firm faggots and gave a more compact and distinct fire signal when lit.[12] The Admiralty found its cheapness attractive because it was reckoned to last about ten years, whereas due to weathering, stacked faggots on the ground needed to be replaced every other year. The impression given by this timescale is that night signals were rarely used.

The captains of the Sea Fencibles were authorised to order fire frames to be erected where they considered them to be necessary, but the cost was not to be more than £2. In some places local estimates for this work came to more, but the limit set was absolute.[13] Along the South Coast, fire frames were built at Lympne, Dungeness, West Wittering, and Cumberland Fort. The frames were not usually approved for signal posts which stood on cliffs or high ground. The Pagham and Selsey stations were on a flat windswept shore and would have found fire frames advantageous, but between them there was a large wood with tall trees which made night signalling almost impossible. High trees and bushes which obscured sight lines between stations were a great nuisance. Their bulk hid the brightness of the fire which could not reach up to the height of the mast to which the daytime signals were hoisted. When complaints were made to the Admiralty, they were usually unable to help, unless the landowner would co-operate for there was no legal authority under which they could insist the trees should be cut down.[14] The only guidance the lieutenants got was to light their station fire where it was most visible. Trouble over this issue was not finally eliminated until 1815, when legislation for the new semaphore stations was passed by Parliament and included a requirement for any obstructions which obscured the sight lines to be removed.[15] Many officers thought that observation at night could be improved if lookouts were issued with night glasses short refracting telescopes which gave clearer vision, although these seem not to have been generally issued.[16] Even Admiral Nelson complained of losing the capture of a brig because he had none at sea.

The orders for alerting the coast during the night to an enemy landing included permission for guns and muskets to be fired from the shore stations where these had been issued. But as there were cannons at only a few posts and musket shots were unlikely to be heard over the long distances between posts the advice seems to have been of limited value. Many lieutenants wanted guns, although usually for use during the day to attract the attention of ships, and sometimes for their own protection. As we have already seen a regular complaint was that ships ignored requests asking for their identity. Although poor visibility was sometimes the cause, inattention by watch keepers, or wilful refusal by captains to comply with Admiralty orders was also suspected. Many in the shore stations thought that if all signal posts had cannon, the boom when they were fired would alert the ships' officers and make it awkward for lax lookouts to make excuses later. Shortly after it was opened the Folkestone and Seaford signal posts asked for cannon for the purpose of calling attention to their signals in bad weather.[17] The Admiralty agreed and some years later Seaford complained that its six pounder gun was too light and a heavier 24 pounder cannon was issued. Beachy Head and Fairlight (Hastings) had a different problem in that they had to signal over 15 miles (24km) in visibility which was often poor during winter and summer and so carronades were supplied. Dunnose on the Isle of Wight also had a gun for in 1812 Captain Spranger reported on its poor condition and it was withdrawn.[18] Cannon were in very short supply in the early years of the French wars, but it seems doubtful whether the Admiralty was ever convinced that there was a strong case for having cannon at all signal posts for this was never done even when the supply position improved. Stations on cliffs or high headlands were certainly given precedence as the gunfire would command attention over a wider area. Signalling at night, using lights, was a chancy undertaking and may have been more successful on moonlight nights when ship and shore positions would have been more visible. What is clear is that if a serious invasion attempt was made by day or night the Admiralty did not intend that their Admirals or ship captains should rely on signals alone. One of their important general orders for all commanders of ships and vessels included the following: **ships and vessels that may be cruising on the enemy's coast who shall observe that the enemy are making preparations to embark, or that they have embarked and sailed, are to despatch a fast sailing vessel (or row boat if the weather will admit) to the nearest port, anchorage or signal station to give notice of same...**[19] Whether or not a messenger rowing across the sea was a practical proposition is perhaps doubtful, but the inclusion of this extreme action surely makes the point that captains were expected to get the news to the English coast using every resource they had. On such a slender thread the safety of England may have depended, but fortunately Napoleon never launched his invasion.

The use of 'Private' signals for challenging the identity of ships at night was also much more difficult than during the day and was probably impossible unless the vessel could be seen or was close inshore. The procedure included a shouted password, although how this worked for signal posts on high headlands is unclear.[20] Possibly there were few challenges at night which could be made and answered effectively. Letters and reports in the Admiralty files suggest that where there was gunfire and signal fires at night there was much confusion as to what was going on. Usually such night time activity was the result of smuggling and efforts to mislead or escape the Riding Officers of the Preventive Service, rather than French ships attempting to attack the coast.

*Night Signals From the Shore No 1*

*Night Signals From the Shore No 2*

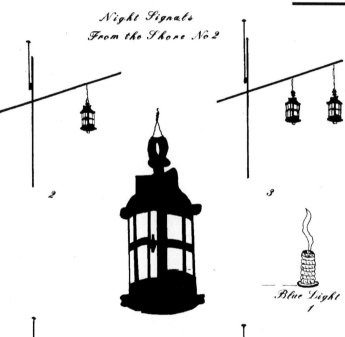

*Blue Light*
*1*

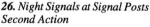

**25.** Night Signals at Signal Posts
First Action

*1 A fire frame designed by Lieutenant Newell of the Teignmouth signal post was sanctioned by the Admiralty for general use. The iron basket held two bundles of furze and stood four feet (1m) high.*

*2 Furze was bought from local farmers by the waggon load costing from 70p to £1.*

*3 The advice from the Admiralty was for the furze to be stored in small stacks roofed with thatch for protection from the weather.*

**26.** Night Signals at Signal Posts
Second Action

*When the burning fire (first action) was acknowledged by adjacent signal posts lanterns with blue lights were hung in different patterns from the signal mast.*

*1 Signal lantern with a blue light. A composition of chemicals burnt in a tube which produces a blue light for 30 seconds.*
*2 Two lights lit successively: Enemy ships have put to sea; or three lights lit similarly: Enemy is approaching the coast.*

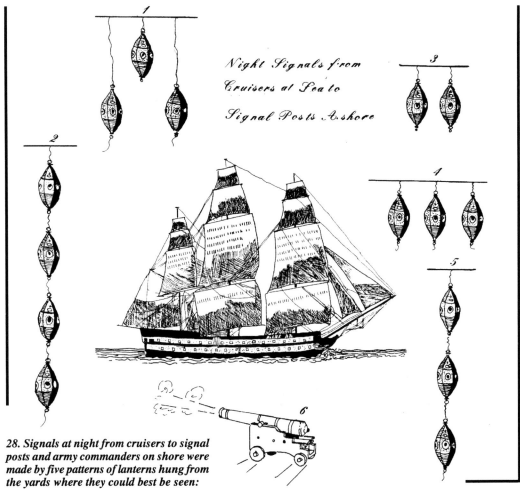

*Night Signals from Cruisers at Sea to Signal Posts Ashore*

**28. Signals at night from cruisers to signal posts and army commanders on shore were made by five patterns of lanterns hung from the yards where they could best be seen:**

1 The enemy is landing to the east or north. (Accompanied by false fires or flares).

2 The enemy is landing to the west or south. (Accompanied by false fires or flares).

3 The enemy's ships have put to sea.

4 The last signal is to be disregarded. (Accompanied by one gun).

5 The enemy is approaching towards the coast.

6 Each of the signals except No 4 was accompanied with a gun firing twice to attract attention. Gunfire was to be repeated at 3-4 minute intervals until acknowledged from the shore.

*3 Two lights lit together: Enemy is landing to the southeast.*

*4 Two lights lit one over the other: Enemy is landing to the east or north.*

*5 Three lights lit together horizontally: the last signal is cancelled.*

*The signal to be repeated every three minutes until answered by adjacent signal posts.*

*27. A signal lamp invented and patented by Mr Brine of Queen Street, Portsea, Portsmouth which was reputed to burn with a bright light for twelve hours. It was fitted into several warships including the Royal William at Spithead. This was one of several types of signal lamps. Most burnt oil.*

# CHAPTER 7

# Defence of the English Coast in 1803

**Fighting with a large army under your command is nowise**
**different from fighting with a smaller one; it is merely a question of instituting signs and signals.**
(The Art of War V.2 Sun Tzu c500 BC).

Tentative plans for the defence of the country had been prepared by the Duke of Richmond, General Dundas and other general staff officers at the turn of the 18th century, but these fell into abeyance when the French threats of 1796 and 1801 receded.[1] When war was resumed following the breakdown of the Peace of Amiens an invasion was expected any day and it was realised that much more had to be done if Napoleon's army of over 100,000 men assembled for crossing the Channel was to be successfully defeated. The mobilisation of thousands of men of the militia and volunteers to support the regular army had to be undertaken quickly. Likewise scores of barracks, gun batteries and magazines for powder, food and forage had to be built.   A further problem was the need to plan the evacuation of the coastal population and livestock to safer areas inland.[2]  In retrospect, 1803 was a watershed year in that major decisions about how the country was to be defended were taken and acted upon within the space of  months. The quantity of orders and correspondence issued by the service and civil authorities shows how seriously the defencelessness of the country was thought to be. An important consequence of this scurry of activity was that the service ministries and civil departments of state needed to co-operate to an unaccustomed extent. This included all levels of society from the Duke of York and his generals, the Admirals, the Lord Lieutenants of the counties, to the magistrates and officials of local communities. Not all was sweetness and light when traditional boundaries of responsibility were upset, and many arguments occurred over who was to pay the bills.

There was recognition, although not agreement over responsibility, for communications to be established throughout the southern counties and on the coast. The term 'communication' was used broadly in documents of the time and embraced telegraphs, signals, beacons, and roads, and any measure that enabled information, troops and supplies to be sent about the country.[3] Political and military chiefs were also in agreement that warnings of the arrival of an invasion force and the activation of measures to stop it had to be strictly monitored, as false alarms would be followed by disastrous consequences.[4]

As explained in the previous chapters, the coast signal stations set up in 1795 by the Admiralty were expected to give the first firm news that the French were on the move and about to invade. This would have served to confirm secret intelligence that was being received from agents and other sources.[5] The defence plans being made from the summer of 1803 also included a warning system by the Home Office to alert the interior of the country.[6] At the same time the Duke of York authorised his generals to  approve the use of new military telegraphs and other signal devices  to connect the several general headquarters of his forces deployed along the South Coast.[7] Extensive research reveals a fascinating account as to how these new signalling systems were developed and with those organised by the Admiralty, helped to unite and inform the forces brought together to defend the southern shores and harbours of Great Britain against attack. How this was accomplished is explained in the next two chapters.

> *29. Field Works*
>
> *1 Portable barrier of timber with spikes for closing roads and gaps in defences.*
>
> *2 Engineers digging entrenchments on the coast.*
>
> *3 Hedges and ditches adapted for infantry positions.*
>
> *4 House and farm walls pierced with musketry loopholes.*
>
> *5 Walls and houses converted into strongpoints.*
>
> *6 An abatis of small branches used to protect a position from attack.*
>
> *7 Trees felled to form an entanglement across a road or open ground.*

**Field Works**

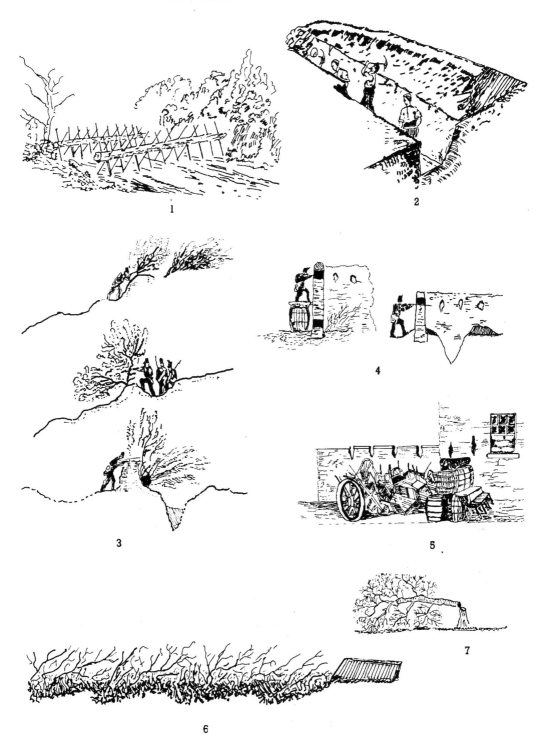

**Permanent Coast Defences**

### 30. Forts

*1 Northcliff Battery, Broadstairs, Kent armed with 24 pounder guns. The magazine is behind the door in the cliff face.*

*2 General Pulteney ordered the refurbishment of the ruins of Camber (Winchelsea) Castle near Rye for artillery. Towers A and B were filled with rubble and heavy cannon mounted. Tower C was reinforced with a brick pillar D to support a new roof for two 6 pounder field guns.*

*3 Seaford (Town?) Battery with five 24 pounder gun positions commanding the sea and the coast east and west. When this sketch was made the guns had been removed.*

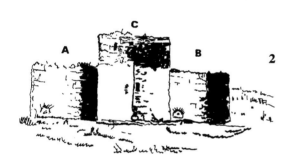

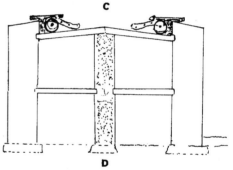

### 31. Batteries

*1 An example of an emplacement for 24 pounder cannon. These were built overlooking the beach every 500 yards (457m) between Eastbourne and Hastings. Later they were replaced with martello towers.*

*2 Each gun battery had an earth covered magazine at the rear for powder and shot.*

*3 The remains of one of two emplacements can still be seen on the banks of the river Brede near Winchelsea. Dips in the earthworks mark the position of embrasures for cannon.*

*4 The Langney entrenchments armed with cannon stretched for 600 yards (548m) and protected the new road from Eastbourne to Hailsham and London. 2,000 men were employed in 1803 in building this work and others in the vicinity of Pevensey.*

1

2

3

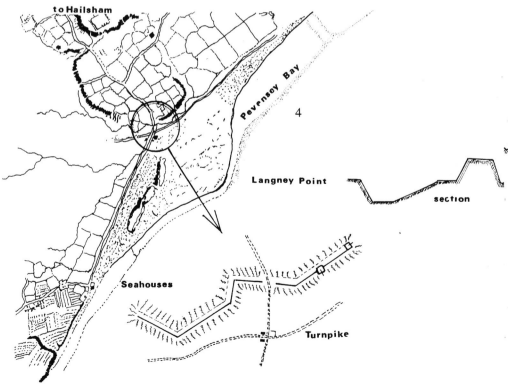

# CHAPTER 8

## Raising the Countryside for War

**Lord Romney and Mr Pitt were here today and
we agreed on establishing beacons for the
interior of the country.** Admiral Keith writing
from Canterbury 12 September 1803.

In devising previous plans for defending the country against an expected invasion of the South Coast the preparations had lacked the urgency and thoroughness with which the problem was tackled in 1803. Never before had the need to coordinate the naval, military and civilian response to the threat been so great and methods of communication so necessary. The actual fighting troops available to General Dundas who commanded the Southern Military District of England, (Kent to Hampshire) included 16,000 men and cavalry in the Regular army, 17,000 Militia, which were men conscripted by the ballot, and 26,000 Volunteers and Yeomanry cavalry. Extra to this total of 60,000 were the specialist services, artillery, engineers and other smaller units.[1]

An immediate problem for General Dundas was how best to call the Militia and Volunteers from their homes and workplaces and assemble them into armed fighting units. Teams of guides with local knowledge of the country, and parties of pioneers to dig trenches and obstruct roads had to be mustered and given orders and tools. A landing on the Kent or Sussex coast was expected, but as no one could foretell where this was likely to take place a cross country movement of large contingents of the defending forces seemed inevitable once battle was joined. Particularly as the small Regular Army (the professional soldiers) was spread so thinly along the many miles of coastline. Workable and speedy lines of communication to alert the defenders and get the Volunteers and Militia to where they could oppose the enemy had to be established.

The first plans by the Home Department included instructions for the evacuation of vulnerable people, the sick and elderly, away from the coast, and the removal of all foodstuffs, horses, carts and boats that might be useful to the enemy. It was soon found, however, that this would be an impractical undertaking as it was not possible to collect enough transport in the time likely to be available. Moreover, refugees would block roads and the destruction of food stocks would result in starvation.[2]

The system of countrywide fire beacons in earlier times described in Chapter 1 had been reinstated as far as was possible during the invasion alerts of the 1790s and 1801, but had fallen into disuse as had the locally based arrangements which supported it. A better and more comprehensive system was clearly needed to integrate all the defence forces, especially those on the coast. The Government acknowledged its responsibility to act, but was reluctant to do so partly because of the cost, but also over doubts as to whether an alarm system could be made to work properly, and the disruption that would ensue from false alarms. General Dundas wrote along these lines in the summer of 1803, when detailed planning was under way. His view was that the only method for raising the alarm was by flying flags from churches and lighting fires and beacons. But he thought measures of this kind would inevitably result in problems whichever was adopted.[3] He was joined in his doubts by General Sir James Craig who was in charge of the defence of counties immediately north of the River Thames.

During July, the Home Department had sent to the generals and Lord Lieutenants detailed instructions about the mobilisation of the Militia, Volunteers and other units. Included amongst these was a document entitled, 'Plan for Establishing a System of Communication throughout each County.'[4] It explained the procedure by which orders from Government would be issued down to parish level, but made no mention of any system of alarms and beacons, apparently leaving this to local initiatives. Meanwhile Generals Dundas and Craig knowing that this was not good enough were busy trying to work out what sort of alarm system was best suited to the areas under their jurisdiction. It soon became clear to them that only a procedure which was uniform throughout the entire country would work efficiently, but that this needed to be backed by decisions and resources at the highest level of government. In September the Prime Minister, General Dundas, Admiral Keith and Lord Romney (Lord Lieutenant of Kent) held a special meeting at Canterbury and agreed to set up a nationwide chain of signal beacons extending inland from the coast.[5] Fortunately authority to requisition land for beacons, batteries and troop encampments was already available under a new Defence of the Realm Act passed by Parliament on 11th June.[6] Up to this point the War Department had given little guidance as to how a beacon system should be set up and managed, and indeed most of its subsequent advice to the rest of the country was based largely on the measures already implemented by generals Dundas and Craig along the Channel coast.[7]

As an invasion on this coastline was more likely than elsewhere the choice of sites and the building of beacons was rushed ahead during the autumn of 1803 and completed by late November. The Home Department expected the Lord Lieutenant in each county and the captains of the Sea Fencibles service to use their local knowledge to prepare a list of suitable beacon sites which would cover the country and link together into a national network of alarms. The sites chosen were then to be agreed by the general in charge and sent for final approval to the Commander-in-Chief, Frederick, Duke of York.[8] At first there was confusion and discontent over who was to pay; the Lord Lieutenants being told that they must do so out of local revenue as Parliament had made no provision to meet the cost.[9] This caused an uproar sufficient to jepardize the proposals because as well as the initial expense of building the beacons there were going to be continuing maintenance costs and regular payments to those employed on guard and watching duties. Within a few weeks a flood of strong protests from the counties led to a change of mind. It was decided to class the beacons as 'field-works' and the generals in charge of each military district were given authority to pay the bills from the contingency funds they held.[10] The army were also asked to oversee the construction of beacons which pleased General Craig who had argued that the Quarter Master General's Department should not be involved because of the delays and difficulties for which that office under Lord Chatham was notorious.[11]

With the beacon programme officially approved and centrally funded the Government then became worried that costs might get out of hand and the War Department wrote to General Craig: **..it is most desirable that their numbers** (of beacons) **should be contracted to the smallest possible limits if they are in sufficient number to alarm the whole extent of the coast, and from 10-16 miles (16-24km) in the rear, perhaps it will suffice as intelligence of the arrival of the enemy will speedily fly when the event really happens.**[12] To this advice, clearly intended to reduce costs, General Craig replied that he thought the purpose of the beacons was to alert the interior of the country and not only the coastline which was already watched by the Admiralty signal posts. He conceded, however, that the number of beacons should be controlled otherwise the expense would be enormous. It was his view that a delay of up to an hour or so of the alarm being given would be of little consequence.[13]

The upshot of this correspondence was that many fewer beacons were built in 1803 than during the Spanish Armada crisis in 1587 and later 17th century invasion scares. All traces of these earlier beacons had long gone, but perhaps not unexpectedly some of the sites for the new beacons were the same.

On the South Eastern coast the number of beacons built followed the advice given by the War Department. In Kent two lines of beacons thrust inland into the heart of the county. A list of 9-14 prospective sites was chosen jointly by Lord Romney, the Lord Lieutenant of Kent, and General Dundas.[14] Twelve beacons were subsequently definitely established; some sources suggest more, or at different places to those shown on the list, but these probably reflected changes made to improve visibility after work had begun. [15]

The arrangement of beacons in Sussex and Hampshire was different; two lines of beacons set well back from the coast, but running parallel with it.[16] Although General Dundas was in overall command, control was delegated to Sir James Pulteney who, although subordinate, was left to take most of the decisions. It was here that problems arose over his relationship with the Lord Lieutenant of Sussex, the Duke of Richmond. As a former Master General of the Ordnance the latter had been much involved with earlier plans for the fortification of the naval ports and the defence of the country. Reluctant to accept a lesser responsibility at this crucial time he found much to criticise in Pulteney's military planning. As a consequence he was uncooperative and declared he would not select any beacon sites or rendezvous points for the Volunteers to assemble at because he thought this should have been done by General Dundas. This matter of his injured pride was apparently not easily resolved and eventually the help of the Commander-in-Chief was sought to placate Richmond's feelings.[17] The Duke was eventually persuaded to work with Pulteney and build the beacons of which fourteen were erected in Sussex.[18]

The Hampshire beacons were not begun until later than those in the other counties because Lord Bolton, the Lord Lieutenant, thought they had been built and having been misinformed it was not until early October that he found out nothing had been done. His plan was for three lines of beacons to straddle the county, and he expected the Admiralty to take responsibility for those on the coast. He seems to have been confused between beacons and signal posts, for the Admiralty had to tell him that they would not pay for the former. Lord Bolton wanted fifteen beacons for Hampshire, but as these included those planned for the coast, possibly fewer were built.[19]

Setting up the beacon system in Kent and Sussex was reported in editions of The Times newspaper, but the places mentioned vary with those in official records which suggests either incorrect reporting or changes when the work was being carried out.[20]

Most of the sites chosen for beacons in Kent were on high downland, 400ft (120m) or more above sea level. Those on the Isle of Thanet and at Aldington and Hawkhurst stood on lower, but prominent, ridges of land about 160-230ft (5070m) above the surrounding countryside. The church towers at Brenchley near Tenterden and Goudhurst were said to have been visible for miles around, the beacon fires being placed in special baskets.

All but three of the beacons in Sussex were built on high points of the South Downs: some 660ft (200m) above sea level. The Upperton Common beacon near Petworth was on a crest further north of the South Downs, and those in St. Leonard's Forest and on Selsfield Common stood out on high points in the Sussex Weald.

Most of the Hampshire and Isle of Wight beacons were also on very hilly sites. Butser Down, to the southwest of Petersfield, is 900ft (270m) high; St Catherine's on the Isle of Wight is 330ft (100m) and Horseshoe Hill west of Broughton village is 500ft (150m). Two low lying sites in Hampshire were on the shores of the Solent and at Beaulieu Heath, although tall columns of smoke from these would have been visible a long way inland because of low ground before the rise of the Downs.

The construction of beacons posed no problems, as it was well within the competence of men working on farms and in the traditional occupations of the time. Newspaper reports infer that some instructions were distributed as to how it should best be done. The precise General Craig told the War Department that furzes stacked around a stake or tree trunk and tied together to stop them being scattered by wind or animals was adequate. However, tar barrels placed on top of the fire caused them to burn better, and smoke balls were also useful.[21] The guidance given to the beacon builders of Kent also mentions constructing a beacon around a tree trunk. The trunk was then to be overlaid with a large stack of furzes or wooden faggots. About eight waggon loads of these would be needed to produce a signal which could be seen ten or twelve miles (18km) distant. If three or four tar barrels were added it was said that the fire could be expected to last for two hours. It was necessary to keep nearby a large quantity of wet straw so as to make a good smoke signal during the day.

In Sussex it was reported that the beacons were made from various combustibles heaped into piles at least 10ft (3m) high.[22] A review of all the reports makes it clear that the fuel most favoured for signal fires at both beacons and signal posts was furze - any form of the spiky broomlike shrub which burns well and grows in abundance on the hills of Southern England.

As to the duration of beacon fires, the advice given to General Brownrigg at the War Department was that it was unlikely that a fire would burn out before its signal had been spotted by watchers on duty at neighbouring posts.[23]

In flat or undulating countryside the only suitable place for the beacon was on top of a high building and this was usually the church tower. The churches at Brenchley, Tenterden and Goudhurst in the Weald of Kent were used in this way. General Dundas did not think this was a very reliable practice and doubtless it was even less welcomed by the vicar.[24] The method usually adopted and thought to be the safest was to fix a framework on the church tower from which an iron basket was hung. Into this a tar barrel was lowered and then ignited.

A problem which resulted in a lot of correspondence between those responsible for setting up the beacon network was about difficulties in finding reliable men who could be trusted to be vigilant and sensible enough to avoid giving false alarms. As most of the male population were already employed in one or other of the defence activities, the choice of trustworthy watchers was limited. Watching out for the invasion signal was a tedious task, and the isolation and exposure of many of the posts made them difficult to reach and uncomfortable to occupy.

General Craig wrote in very unfavourable terms about the lowly class of person likely to be hired as beacon watchers and doubted whether they could be trusted to be alert and observant enough. He wanted to engage Chelsea pensioners or other retired soldiers about whose reliability he seemed completely satisfied, and although the War Department had no objection they doubted whether these would come forward in sufficient numbers. Instead they recommended that men from the Militia and Volunteer units should be used.[25] Lord Bolton told the Home Department that he thought their offer to pay only nine old pence for each day's duty would be little inducement as the type of person they preferred could earn three times as much by daily labour elsewhere.[26] The Government recognised that there were likely to be difficulties over engaging suitable watchers at the beacons, but left the Lord Lieutenants and district generals to resolve the matter by advising them to make the best arrangements they could. Thus in the southern counties Militia and Volunteer soldiers were recruited; a soldier and two men being assigned to each beacon. In 1805 to save money the War Department reduced the numbers to one man which was an unpopular measure because the terms of their engagement guaranteed their pay, even though they were often unsuitable for duties elsewhere. About this time regular married soldiers in the Gosport area assigned to beacon duties earned five old pence daily on top of their regimental pay. At some beacons the watchers were paid from army funds administered by the district generals. Not all these men were soldiers, some being local civilians living near to the beacons they tended.[27] Payments to the watchers appear in many old militia records and account books. At St. Catherine's Hill near Winchester the guards were ordered to: **strictly attend the beacon and hut, and to be civil to the Winchester College boys, but not to let them enter the hut or take straw from the beacon.**[28]

To enable the sergeant in charge of the Sussex beacons to see these signals he was issued with one of the smaller telescopes made by Messrs Dolland of London. The telescope was handed over by an army captain who visited each site to train the men in their duties. Similar arrangements were made in other counties.[29]

Towards the end of September 1803, General Craig told the War Department that with the onset of winter the beacon watchers needed better shelter than the tents they had been living in.[30] This led to plans for a standard hut being drawn up. It was to be a building of sufficient strength to resist the wear and tear of winter weather. The dimensions were 14ft by 10ft (4m by 3m).It was certainly a basic structure and was roughly built with turf walls and thatched roof. Its most solid part was a brick fireplace and chimney. In one corner of the hut was a wooden ledge to be used as a bed. This was 7ft (2.3m) wide in which at least two men could sleep comfortably. The huts were expected to be built for about £8, although the district general had discretion to spend up to £10: **so that proper accommodation may be given.**[31] It was probably a hut of this type which Lieutenant Gardner of the Royal Navy mistook for the Hastings signal post when he took up duty there in January 1806. There was a beacon nearby and he spoke to soldiers near the hut to ask the way. His comments were not favourable:. **When I got to the summit of Fairlight Down the first object that struck me was a hut built of turf in a ruinous state. Taking a turn around the premises I thought I would look inside. I did so, but backed out again in a hurry from the filth and wretchedness.**[32]

Periodically a check was made on the state of the beacons and huts and a report was sent to the War Department. A return of the Sussex beacons shows the date of the inspection, details of repairs wanted, and the name and occupation of the person responsible. The beacons at Jevington (Mr Barnard), Upperton Common (John Colbrook), and Rooks Hill (Mr Asted) were maintained by farmers. George Marshall who was a carpenter tended the Duncton beacon and the inn keeper of the Richmond Arms at St Leonard's Forest looked after the one there. Charles Camfield, another inn keeper was responsible for the Crowborough beacon and that at Brightling was in the care of John Lovell from the mill nearby.[33]

The chaos and panic likely to occur if the beacons were lighted prematurely was so disturbing that the Commander-in-Chief held discussions with generals Craig and Dundas and they decided that to reduce the risk of confusion, the giving of orders to fire the primary beacons had to be very tightly controlled. It was perhaps too much to expect that mistakes would never happen. In Essex there was a potentially serious incident one evening when the blaze of a large fire was seen on the coast. The troops were mobilised and a messenger was sent to find out what was happening. He reported back that it was: **the ignorant and imprudent act of some person burning weeds and bean straw.**[34] In another instance one of the beacons close to Southampton was set alight about 10 p.m. on a Monday night in January. Orders were given to raise the Volunteers and they stayed on alert until 4 a.m. the following morning when they were stood down, the alarm having been found to be a mistake.[35]

The approach of enemy transports carrying infantry was to be signalled along the coast by the chain of Admiralty signal posts displaying signals numbered 5-8 (see Chapter 5). The lieutenants in charge had been told that if they flew these signals they were to tell the nearest military commander and also the captains of the Sea Fencibles immediately.[36] To make sure this was done the War Department, apparently acting on a suggestion from Lord Keith, agreed to station dragoons at the more important signal posts closest to the headquarters of generals commanding the armies on the South Coast.[37] It is unclear how many posts had dragoons attached, but two were certainly sent to Fairlight in Sussex and at the North Foreland post in Kent. The dragoons lived in rough huts similar to those built for the beacon guards. They were expected to ride with despatches to General Spencer in camp at Hastings and General Auchmutz encamped outside Ramsgate.[38]

As part of the tight control enforced over giving a signal for the primary beacons to be lit the decision was to be made by the general commanding in the area. It was up to him to evaluate the quality of the information he received from the signal posts, his messengers and other sources. Once he had ordered the beacons to be fired the men with their arms would gather at their nominated assembly places and the civil authorities would be put in a state of readiness.[39]

In East Sussex, Sir James Pulteney had arranged for the beacons at Fairlight, Hollingbury, Chanctonbury and the one on St Roche Hill to be fired first.[40] Lighting the beacon at Fairlight near Hastings would prompt a response from the one at Hawkhurst so alerting the Kent chain of beacons and General Dundas whose headquarters was inland in Canterbury.

In West Sussex the signal from the beacon on St Roche Hill which is north of Chichester would have been spotted by watchers on the Butser and Portsmouth Hills so causing the Hampshire chain of beacons to be ignited.

The army commanders on the coast had also received clear orders from General Dundas to report any attempted landings directly and immediately to him personally. Dundas stipulated that important news was to be carried by an officer who could be trusted to give a reliable appraisal of the tactical situation on the coast.[41]

This officer was to travel fast using army horses, but if these were not available he was to hire post horses. The orders giving directions about the routes to be followed are carefully written and are reproduced in full at the end of this chapter.

One of the problems of major concern to the army commanders was whether the beacons should be lighted at night. Generals Craig and Dundas emphasised to the War Department that to do so would increase the likelihood of false alarms and in the confusion that would arise might result in troops being sent to the wrong part of the coast. Eventually the sense of this view was accepted by General Brownrigg at the War Department and he replied saying: **The prohibition of beacons being lighted at night appears proper.**[42] However, the passing of night signals between the Admiralty signal posts on the coast was not curtailed, a major difference between the two systems being that these were manned by trained seamen under the supervision of an officer.

There were many requests from Lord Lieutenants responsible for the beacon system asking for information about signals received at the Admiralty signal posts. The request was usually made to the captain of the Sea Fencibles, a naval officer also in charge of the signal posts in his district. His instructions were to refuse such requests as the Admiralty was worried that misuse or misunderstanding of their signals might perhaps adversely affect naval operations.[43] As an example of the stringency with which these orders were carried out, General Pulteney in charge of the Sussex armies was refused information by Lieutenant Norris at the Beachy Head signal post. Tempers flared and there were high level representations by the Commanderin-Chief to the Admiralty on his behalf. The outcome of this indignant exchange was that the orders to naval officers at the signal posts were changed and they were told that they must pass to the generals on the coast whatever message or intelligence they had about enemy movements.[44]

By the end of 1803 most of the beacons were fully manned with watchers, and the Government had to decide on the signals to be used to alert the countryside. Simplicity was reckoned to be most important, but to allow for some flexibility to meet local circumstances each general was asked to agree upon a signal with the Lord Lieutenant of the district.[45] Although this made allowance for regional preferences it is evident from War Department letters that lighting a single beacon to produce a tall column of smoke rather than a flame was the alarm signal expected to be adopted. This was to be achieved by adding damp grass or straw to the fire. Smoke balls could also be lit and these were expected to burn for thirty minutes. The signal which could be given by a single beacon did of course have its limitations. But even in the flat countryside of Essex where it was proposed to build a line of double beacons, General Craig's opinion was that this was unnecessary as well as being more expensive. He did, however, recommend that large red flags should be hoisted on church steeples as a supplementary warning measure.[46]

Great care was taken to ensure the system worked and beacons were test fired during daytime with watchers at a distance being asked: **whether they could discern the smoke of them or not.**[47]

General Dundas had a special set of regulations about beacons printed and circulated to all commanders in Kent and Sussex and these began with the order: **Upon the beacons being fired, or other intelligence of an enemy approaching the coast, the Volunteer corps of cavalry and infantry will immediately assemble at their different places of rendezvous.**[48]

Several meetings took place between the War Department and the Admiralty for the purpose of agreeing a signal to pass the alarm from the naval signal posts to the nearest beacon which was often some distance inland. The Admiralty were insistent that such a signal should be completely different from those used to communicate with ships and other signal posts on the coast. The Commander-in-Chief, also anxious to reduce confusion and well aware of the limitations of many of those tending the beacons, argued that only one signal of a general nature signifying an attack would be practical. This he thought should be that the enemy were approaching and landing on the shore.[49] The Admiralty agreed and sent him copies of one which had been worked out by them in conjunction with General Craig for use on the East Coast.[50] Unfortunately precisely what this signal was seems not to have survived, but it may have been a written despatch delivered by messenger.

General Dalrympne commanding in Northern England doubted the wisdom of the naval signal posts being told to communicate direct with the beacons. He complained that it would turn out to be impractical: **because the sergeant in charge of the beacons would never be brought to comprehend, and by which they would be perpetually misled.**[51] The outcome of discussion over signals between the signal stations on the coast and the beacons seems to have been short lived, for within weeks the War Department agreed to post dragoons at those Admiralty signal posts close to each general's headquarters. The messengers were to ride immediately to the general with news of the approaching French invasion ships. This was by far the most sensible arrangement for it reduced the chance of mistakes, especially as it was to be solely upon the district general's authority that the beacons were to be fired.

The taking of land on which to build the beacons was generally accepted by farmers and landowners without dispute although one incident in Sussex caused a commotion which rose to the highest level of government for settlement. Mr Charles Goring, a landowner of Wiston Park near Washington, protested about putting a beacon on land he owned at nearby Chanctonbury Ring. Possibly he was worried about damage that might be caused to a fine clump of beech trees planted there forty three years earlier. He wrote to Charles Yorke, Secretary of State for the Home Department, who sent his complaint to General Pulteney with a request: **that he should pay every attention to the remonstrance of this gentleman which can be done without impediment to His Majesty's Service.** The beacon was built, but doubtless its position on the hilltop was changed to meet Mr Goring's wishes.[52] The trees on Chanctonbury survive to this day and are visible 30 miles (38km) away which confirms how effective these high hills were for signalling further inland when no other methods were available.

Orders were issued during the autumn of 1803 for all the beacons throughout the southern counties to be lit to test their effectiveness of the alarm system. The results were found to be satisfactory and reports show that it was possible to signal warning of an approaching invasion over a distance of 100 miles (161km) in fifteen minutes.[53]

An assessment of the beacon system as a means of alerting the countryside, calling out the Militia and Volunteer army, and setting in motion arrangements for moving the civil population from the coast must be that it was well organised and carefully controlled to avoid false alarms. Because the measure was funded centrally by the War and Home Departments it was as comprehensive and uniform in operation as the resources of the time permitted. If it had been necessary to put the plan into action it would probably have worked well, always of course making allowances for human error.

For its own advance warning of a serious attempt by Napoleon to invade, the Government relied on an almost constant flow of secret intelligence from its agents in France, from smugglers, fishermen, and from reports from Royal Navy ships blockading the Channel ports. From time to time evaluation of this information led to advance briefings being issued to admirals at sea and generals on the South Coast. For example, In February 1803 General Dundas received the message: **gives reason to suppose that it is the enemy's purpose to attack us soon after the approaching equinox as the wind and weather will permit...and it is Mr Secretary Yorke's confidential opinion that if he attacks us at all he may be expected to arrive by the first south east and south by west wind after the next equinoxial gale.** [54]

Notwithstanding the effort put into the creation of as good a beacon warning system as was possible, it is clear from the views expressed by generals in their letters to the War Department that they were both reluctant and unlikely to give orders to deploy the bulk of their forces until they received despatches confirming the place and size of an enemy landing. They expected this vital information to come to them post haste and to be carried by officers from regiments stationed directly on the coastline. Instructions to this end were given by General Dundas and General Pulteney.

The end of the beacon system is obscure and it probably just fell into disuse. It seems to have been discontinued first in those areas of the country remote from the coast. In Susssex beacons were still being maintained until at least 1810-11 and possibly later.[55] It is apparent from letters of the time that their continuance rested on whether the district general was prepared to pay the bills for watchers and upkeep from his budget; some were less convinced of the usefulness of the system than others.[56]

The temporary nature of both beacons and huts meant that neither lasted for long and any contemporary illustrations and drawings in local archives depicting this interesting aspect of British history would be a rare find indeed if they exist.

# Beacon Sites and Communications to London
## from the South East Coast 1803-1810

### Kent Beacon Stations

| | |
|---|---|
| Centre of the Isle of Thanet* | Site unconfirmed, but probably near to Minster where there was an Armada beacon. |
| Barham Down | On the eastern edge of the hillside close to Barham village. |
| South Foreland  Signal Post* | This was the Little Cornhill naval signal post on the hill near Wanstone Farm. |
| Folkestone Signal Post* | Near to the old turnpike on the Dover road above Eastwear Bay. |
| Aldington Castle* | A small hill now known as Aldington Knoll 9km west of Hythe. |
| Shottenden Hill | A hill overlooking the village 13km southwest of Canterbury. |
| Hothfield Common | Misnamed Northfield Heath. Between Westwell and Pluckley villages. |
| Tenterden+ | The beacon was on top of St Michael's Church which stands on high ground. |
| Coxheath | An area of heathland 5km south of Maidstone where there was a large military camp in 1803. |
| Birling | The beacon was on a ridge of the North Downs above the villages of Birling and Ryarsh; 11km northwest of Maidstone. |
| Boxley | On top of the North Downs above Boxley village and in sight of Birling beacon. |
| Brenchley Church | All Saints, Brenchley stands on the crest of a hill. |
| Goudhurst Church | The Church of St Mary's stands on a hill top and can be seen from afar. |
| Hawkhurst+ | The beacon stood on land known as Highgate on the edge of the village. |

\* These were primary beacons which were lit first and from which the others took their cue.
\+ The Tenterden and Hawkhurst beacons connected with the chain of beacons in Sussex.
Sources: PRO WO 30/56; HO 50/74: AM 6911-4-7.

### Sussex Beacon Stations

| | |
|---|---|
| Fairlight Down*+ | Close to the naval signal post at Fairlight east of Hastings. |
| Jevington Down* | North of Beachy Head and near the windmill which once stood on the Down. |
| Firle Beacon | A high hill above the village of West Firle. |
| Mount Harry | A hill above the village of Offham northwest of Lewes. |
| Hollingbury Castle* | The beacon site was within an earthwork above Moulsecoomb Wild Park now within the environs of Brighton. |
| Wolstonbury | An isolated hill crowned with an earthwork close to Poynings and Pyecombe villages near Brighton. |
| Chanctonbury Ring* | A hill above Washington village north of Worthing. |
| Duncton Beacon | A hill above Duncton village south of Petworth. |
| St Roche Hill *+ | Otherwise known as the Trundle adjacent to Goodwood Race course north of Chichester. |
| Upperton Common | A high ridge of land close to the park at Petworth. |
| St Leonard's Forest | A place known as Stone Lodge within the forest which lies to the east of Horsham town. |

| | |
|---|---|
| Selsfield Common | A stretch of common land between Turner's Hill and Hoathly east of Crawley town. |
| Crowborough Beacon | A hill on the outskirts of Crowborough town. |
| Brightling | On Brightling Down south of Burwash village. |

* Primary beacons were those which were fired first and from which others took their lead. They were usually on or close to the coast.
+ The Fairlight beacon passed on or received the alarm signal from the Kent chain of beacons and the one at St Roche Hill connected with beacons in Hampshire.
Sources: PRO WO 30/69; WO 30/81; ESRO SAS/GM.

## Hampshire Beacon Stations

| | |
|---|---|
| Portsdown Hill*+ (Portsmouth) | Close to the naval telegraph station between the present Forts Widley and Purbrook. |
| Bere Forest | Site uncertain, but probably on the borders of East Bere Forest. It was said to be near to Winchester. Beacon Hill 2km west of Warnford completes the chain. |
| Town Hill | Now Townhill Park midway between South Stoneham and West End on the east bank of the River Itchen. |
| Beaulieu Heath* | The site was probably on higher ground at Hatchet Moor. |
| St Catherine's Hill* (Christchurch) | A hill 5km northwest of Christchurch town. |
| Point on the coast between Calshot and Lymington | Location uncertain, but possibly Calshot, Stone, or Needs Oar Point. |
| Butser Hill+ | A high hill 5km southwest of Petersfield. |
| Wickham | Near West Lodge, northeast of Rooksbury Park School. A naval telegraph station was nearby. |
| Chilworth Hill | Either at Toot Hill on which there was also a naval telegraph or close to Chilworth, 4km SE of Romsey. Next to a lodge owned by Mr Serle. |
| Stoney Cross | A place in the New Forest 5km northwest of Lyndhurst. |
| Moyles Court | Said to have been sited near a summerhouse on the edge of Rockford Common 3km north of Ringwood. |
| St Catherine's Hill+ (Winchester) | Close to Twyford Down 2km southeast of Winchester. |
| Farley Hill+ | Almost certainly Farley Mount at the end of the Pitt Down range of hills 8km west of Winchester. |
| Horseshoe Hill+ | At the western edge of Brougham Down 3km west of Brougham village. |

* These were probably primary beacons, although confirmation that this was so is still awaited from local records.
 + These beacons passed on or received the signal from adjacent counties.
Sources: PRO HO 50/72; HO 50/107; HO 50/135.

## Isle of Wight

Information about where fire beacons were set up on the Isle of Wight in 1803 is hard to find. There would have been fewer than during the Spanish Armada crisis because official warnings would have been signalled to Portsmouth and the mainland by the naval signal posts. However, fire beacons to call out the volunteers and alert the civil population would still have been needed. It is likely that the most important of these would have been placed in highly visible places close to the Admiralty signal posts on Ashey Down, St Catherine's Hill, Chale and at the Needles.

## COMMMUNICATION OF INTELLIGENCE TO LONDON

On 17th July 1803 General David Dundas issued an order from his Headquarters near Chatham. It set out how and to what centres news of an enemy approaching the coast or landing on the shore should be sent. The order is reproduced below with the exception of the mileage between intermediate places on the routes to the destinations mentioned:-

**Should an enemy appear or land in great Force at, near, or between:**
About Rye or Hastings
**Communication must be made to Hythe, also direct by Hawkhurst to Maidstone, Chatham, and by Ore to the Westward.**
From Bexhill to Eastbourne
**To Lewes, Brighton and Ore.**
Eastbourne to Brighton
**To Ore, Brighton, Lewes and Chichester.**
Brighton
**To Ore, Chichester, and direct to Chatham and direct to London.**
Neighbourhood of Shoreham to Chichester
**To Portsmouth, Brighton, Ore and direct to London and Winchester.**
(The next section of the order makes clear the importance of news of the invasion being sent separately and directly to London).
**Communication of the above Event, happening from the Isle of Thanet to Dungeness, will be made through Chatham to London.**
From Rye to Bexhill
**Direct to London.**
From Bexhill to Seaford
**As Sir James Pulteney shall direct, to London.**
From Seaford to Shoreham
**From Brighton to London.**
From Arundel to Chichester
**Direct to London.**
**The Commanding Officer at Maidstone will give whatever information he receives to the camp at Coxheath; he is therefore to be acquainted accordingly.**
**Intelligence of great importance and such as demand the immediate movement of Troops, or must create universal alarm must be accurate and distinct, and not too hastily sent off in the first instance.**
**On very important occasions officers who can give personal explanation in addition to written Intelligence will be sent off, who may be provided with orderly Horses as far as they go, and then proceed by hired Post ones.**
**All such Intelligence from Chichester to Rye, when it reaches Ore, is to be sent to Chatham from Ore.**
**All such Intelligence from Dungeness to Margate when it reaches Hythe is to be sent to Chatham.**
**Besides the special Notifications as above mentioned, when the attack of the Enemy is ascertained by their coming to an Anchor, or preparing to Land, universal Intelligence cannot be too widely circulated.**

**Intelligence of the above nature must be as minute and circumstantive as possible, of the number and nature of the Enemy Vessels, and of any apparent circumstance that can tend to give an idea of the Troops they may contain, as so much depends on a knowledge of this circumstance.**

Source: PRO WO 30/81 Document 2

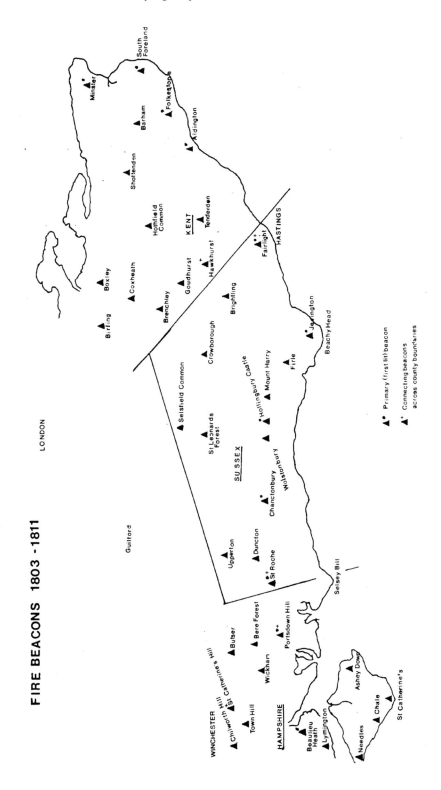

32. *This map shows the sites of the fire beacons established by the Lord Lieutenants in Kent, Sussex and Hampshire and paid for from War Office funds. Not shown on the map are those Hampshire beacons at St. Catherine's, (Christchurch), Stoney Cross, (New Forest) and Moyles Court on Rockford Common. The Isle of Wight beacons are probable sites.*

FIRE BEACONS 1803 - 1811

LONDON

Guilford

Minster

South Foreland

Barham

Folkestone

Aldington

Shottenden

Hothfield Common

KENT

Tenderden

HASTINGS

Fairlight

Boxley

Coxheath

Brenchley

Goudhurst

Hawkhurst

Brightling

Birling

Crowborough

Selsfield Common

Hollingbury Castle

Mount Harry

Firle

Jevington

Beachy Head

St Leonards Forest

SUSSEX

Chanctonbury

Wolstonbury

Upperton

Duncton

St Roche

Selsey Bill

WINCHESTER

Chilworth Hill

St Catherine's Hill

Butser

Bere Forest

Wickham

Town Hill

Portsdown Hill

HAMPSHIRE

Beaulieu Heath

Lymington

Needles

Chale

Ashey Down

St Catherine's

▲• Primary (first lit) beacon

▲+ Connecting beacons across county boundaries

33. To build a beacon wood and furze were piled around a central post for support and topped with a tar barrel. About eight waggon loads of such fuel were needed for a fire to burn for two hours and be seen 10 miles (16km) distant. A white flag marked the site of the beacon.

34. In some villages where the church offered exceptional visibility over the surrounding countryside tar barrels were hoisted to the top of the tower and burnt.

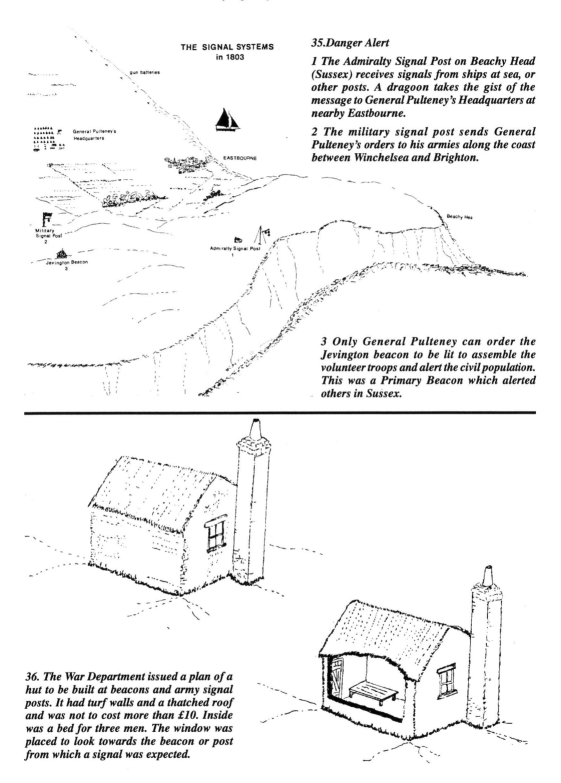

THE SIGNAL SYSTEMS
in 1803

gun batteries

General Pulteney's
Headquarters

EASTBOURNE

Beachy Head

Military
Signal Post
2

Admiralty Signal Post
1

Jevington Beacon
3

**35. Danger Alert**

**1 The Admiralty Signal Post on Beachy Head (Sussex) receives signals from ships at sea, or other posts. A dragoon takes the gist of the message to General Pulteney's Headquarters at nearby Eastbourne.**

**2 The military signal post sends General Pulteney's orders to his armies along the coast between Winchelsea and Brighton.**

**3 Only General Pulteney can order the Jevington beacon to be lit to assemble the volunteer troops and alert the civil population. This was a Primary Beacon which alerted others in Sussex.**

**36. The War Department issued a plan of a hut to be built at beacons and army signal posts. It had turf walls and a thatched roof and was not to cost more than £10. Inside was a bed for three men. The window was placed to look towards the beacon or post from which a signal was expected.**

# CHAPTER 9

# The Earlier History of Military Signals in Southern England

**It is rather surprising that an art so simple as that of conveying ideas by means of signals, so well understood in remote antiquity, and practised even by savages, should have made such little progress in its improvement, that it may be said to have remained in its original rude state nearly down to our own times...** Encyclopaedia Britannica (Telegraph), 1824.

Unlike the navy where communication between ships was difficult if not impossible without some form of signalling, the British army of the 18th century was content with measures which had served it well in conflicts abroad and on mainland Europe. In battle the movement of troops was controlled by trumpets, bugle calls and messengers. Communication over longer distances was by mounted officers and runners who took messages either written down or delivered verbally. Although not always fast or error free commanders found these direct methods more reliable than various signalling devices which were suggested from time to time. Most official British army historians claim that signalling over distance was not used until the Peninsular War in 1810, but this is not so as this chapter will explain.

It was the unusual circumstances of regiments being deployed along hundreds of miles of coastline from The Wash to the Isle of Wight and awaiting a French invasion, which led to the need for a system of signals which would assist communications between the generals commanding the troops. In some respects it was a development made necessary by the need to fight, for the first time since the Spanish Armada crisis, along the coastline of Britain. It was also to get the support and encouragement of the Duke of York, who foresaw the difficulties of controlling the defence of the country from London without speedy communication.

Due to the novelty of signalling across country, a number of different methods were tried including apparatus with moveable arms on carts and portable displays of flags and pennants flown from high masts. They were all included within the definition at the time of military telegraphs, which makes it sometimes difficult to be sure when studying senior officers' correspondence of the method being used.

At the end of the 18th century the Admiralty and the War Department took part in a joint experiment with the use of a signalling device involving 'white lights'.[1] The venture apparently went well for when answering questions about measures for the defence of Southern England against a feared French attack, the Duke of York then a colonel, said that apparatus comprising reverberatory lamps and white lights was to be issued by the Ordnance Department to land stations likely to be called upon to make signals.[2] He also asked the Admiralty to appoint men accustomed to using these signals to act with the army.[3] Reverberatory lamps were an early type of concave copper reflecting lamp. With the help of 9-10 inch (229-254mm) reflectors, well polished and silvered, a strong white light could be produced which was reckoned to be of equivalent brightness to average noonday sunlight. The white light could be seen up to 15 miles (24km) and even greater distances depending on the size of reflector used. It was this type of lamp that had been used by Major General Roy when he was surveying a trigonometrical connection between Dover and Calais to fix the meridians in 1787.[4] White lights were produced from a composition of powdered ingredients of 28 parts of nitre, 4 parts of sulphur and 2 parts of orpient (trisulphate of arsenic). The mixture was burnt in copper cups and lit by portfires.

How widely these lights were used by the army is unclear, but perhaps not much. It seems that the code of signals used was simple and agreed locally, and it probably consisted of a number of flashes from one or more lamps on stands to indicate a limited number of warnings or military orders. This is not the only time 'white lights' were used, for in 1803 when the French were threatening invasion the matter came up again. General Dalrympne wrote to the War Department to remind them that his engineers were using a double revolving light which could not be mistaken for any other fire, especially as the signalmen worked to a set of rules written to exclude mistakes. An advantage was that he did not think these lights were more costly than other methods.[5]

It seems that from early in his career, the Duke of York realised the advantages an organised system of signalling could have for the military. His interest at this time was to foreshadow the support he was to give it later when he was appointed to the post of Commander-in-Chief.

Innumerable inventors with ideas for new or improved signalling devices usually sent their proposals to the Admiralty who were thought to be more interested in the subject because of the difficulties of communicating at sea. One which got some early attention was Richard Edgeworth who had invented a Tellograph. This machine consisted of upright supports on which triangular pointers moved like the hands of a clock; the position of each pointer indicating a number. He had also developed a portable version which could be operated by one man. Edgeworth arranged a demonstration before the Duke and Admiralty officials in October 1786. The Duke was invited to these trials as it was known he was keen to acquire a signalling device which could be used by military reconnoitring parties to send information of enemy movements back to the main army. After the demonstration he complimented Edgeworth on his ingenuity, who returned home with the impression that the Government would buy his invention. However, this was not to be for the Admiralty decided it was not interested and the Duke declined to give the venture any further encouragement.[6] Almost certainly he acted on the advice of his advisor the Reverend Gamble who had made a study of all the various signalling systems he could find. Gamble later wrote about his doubts as to whether the precise position of the minute graduations in Edgeworth's machine which spelled out the figures could be accurately determined in poor visibility or strong winds which would make it hard to keep a telescope steady.[7] Although the Edgeworth system was used in Ireland between Dublin and Galway for about four years from its establishment in 1804, it was never adopted elsewhere in Britain by the military or naval establishments.[8] Furthermore the Reverend Gamble was unsuccessful in his efforts to persuade the Admiralty that his design of shutter telegraphs for the London, Deal and Portsmouth routes was better than the one they had bought from Lord George Murray (Chapter 10). However, he was to have more luck over negotiations with the War Department for a completely different type of signalling. He called this apparatus a radiated telegraph and designed several models some of which being portable were better suited for an army on the march. Gamble wrote that he had come to the conclusion that the general principles of the radiated telegraph were superior because they represented: **theory corrected by practice and experience.** The radiated telegraph signalled by five wooden rays or arms and was in reality what was later to be recognised as a semaphore, although it had been preceded by the French tachygraphe three years earlier. Some years after Gamble's death, Sir John Barrow the celebrated Admiralty secretary, conceded that Gamble was right in advocating the superiority of this type of signalling over other methods.[9] Having decided that his radiated telegraph gave the clearest signal from afar he thought the mechanical design of the telegraph was incidental and developed several versions. One had five fixed extendable arms which shot out from a square framework, their angle indicating numbers 1-5 enabling 31 orders or letters to be signalled. A second, more portable apparatus, also had five arms each with a roundel at their end to improve the clarity of their angle. The arms were fixed to a circular plate and mounted on top of a pole making it extremely portable. The arms were hoisted into position by ropes or chains which when released dropped them out of sight. It was anticipated that the expense to the army of providing this machine, to use in the field, would be under £50. A breakdown of the cost would be £12.50 for the telegraph machine; £8.50 for strengthening an old cart with coach wheels and an iron axle; £10.50 for poles, ropes and ironwork, and £12.50 for two Admiralty telescopes. A bell tent for three men and a horse to draw the cart would be extra.

Using his influence with the Duke of York in 1795, Gamble was ordered to ship one of these machines to the West Indies, presumably to evaluate whether it would be useful for troops engaged in reconnaissance work.[10] General Sir Ralph Abercromby commanding a force of 15,000 men had been ordered to set sail to quell a major insurrection of indigenous Negroes in the Windward Islands. Gamble says that he went down to Portsmouth in September 1795 to wait upon General Abercromby and gave his radiated telegraph into the care of General Simcoe. This general was known for his interest in scouting and reconnaissance parties which was why he may have been selected for this task. At the time there was a great deal of political pressure for this expedition to get under way, but the departure was delayed by poor preparations and deficient equipment. Tragedy struck when it finally left Portsmouth in November under the command of Admiral Hugh Christian, for it ran into storms so severe that over one hundred ships were lost, sunk, wrecked ashore or captured by the French.[11]

It is not absolutely clear from Gamble's second Essay on Signals published two years later which telegraph machine went to the West Indies, but it was almost certainly the portable version for mounting on a pole. He also makes no reference to how it fared on active service and it seems more than likely that it was lost at sea and never reached the West Indies.

Encouraged by the order to supply General Abercromby's force with one of his radiated telegraph machines, Gamble continued with his interest in signalling to get it more widely adopted. The success of his efforts caused the Duke of York to appoint a committee to evaluate its utility and report back to him personally. During the winter of 1797, or perhaps a month or so later, for the Committee's benefit he carried out trials of his radiated telegraph near Woolwich, and signalled over a distance of 4-5 miles (6-8km) to another at Blackheath. Further trials involved signalling from Woolwich to a receiving station on Shooters Hill about three miles away.

The Committee was a prestigious one, chaired by General Charles Cornwallis who had been appointed

Master General of the Ordnance in 1795 with special responsibilities to supervise the defence of England against a threatened French attack. His overview of the Gamble experiments was one of his last tasks before he was sent to Ireland as Viceroy and Commander-in-Chief. Other members of this committee included senior field officers (men with experience in battle) chiefly from the Royal Artillery headquarters in Woolwich. They were generals Drummond, Walker, Borthwick and Lloyd; colonels Stewart, Huddleston, Broomfield and Tread(?) and lieutenant colonels Stevens, Douglas and Smith. In their report the committee endorsed the usefulness of the radiated telegraph. They, however, were careful to urge caution in suggesting where it could best be used and referred to Gamble's reservation about the need for clear lines of sight between stations. They made the point that its success in the field depended on the kind of country in which an army was fighting and where: **from such positions as would probably be occupied by troops in desultory movements. In these cases the rapidity of communication will greatly depend on the judgement in choice of ground.**[12] Satisfied with the Committee's overall approval the Duke of York wrote to William Wyndham (Secretary at War) stressing the advantages of a radiated telegraph to an army in the field:-

> **Be well aware of the great advantages which in cases of emergency may be derived from immediate communication by means of Telegraphs. I beg to recommend to you that an immediate experiment be made as to portable ones presented by the Reverend Gamble in stations which may appear most eligible for the purpose of ascertaining their utility.**[13]

The next development seems to have been a suggestion by Gamble to the Duke of York that a military telegraph should be set up from London to the coasts of Essex, Kent, Sussex or Hampshire. With the Duke's approval he was then given an order to build one to a point on the East coast.[14] A memorandum from Gamble which included an estimate amounting to £600 for twelve portable radiated telegraphs, but not the cost of surveying the route, was then sent with the Duke's endorsement to Mathew Lewis in the office of the Secretary at War on 23rd April 1798.[15] We are told nothing further as to whether the work was undertaken at this time and as will be explained later, it seems to have been delayed for a year or two. Clearly the Duke continued to support the radiated telegraph for army use, for in August of the same year he ordered Gamble to establish a temporary line of radiated telegraphs between London and a camp near Windsor. For this project, Gamble put in a request for £200 from which we can infer, that at £50 for each portable machine and carriage to transport it, four were needed. Again the Secretary for War was asked to make payment.[16] There is no mention of any telegraph communication in the Windsor Castle, Royal Archives,[17] but a new camp for three Guards' regiments was opened in August 1798 close to King's Beech Hill, two miles northeast of Bagshot village and about four miles from Windsor Great Park.[18] The intervening country to London is now heavily obstructed with buildings and it is impossible to decide the route the signals would have taken from the Capital, but the distance of 21 miles (34km) could have been within the signalling range of four portable stations. In spite of the flurry of activity over the Reverend Gamble's telegraph in 1798 and his continuing interest in the subject, no further accounts of his invention were published nor was any reference made to how successful it had been in operation. The conclusion must be that its usefulness did not amount to much. Meanwhile, the Duke of York was engaged on more pressing business. Following his disastrous attempt to invade Holland in 1799, he concentrated his efforts as Commander-in-Chief in carrying out much needed reforms of the army. These included the formation of a Royal Staff Corps of technical men to provide engineering support which was found to be lacking in the campaign in the Netherlands.[19] There was no mention, however, of their undertaking signalling duties at this time which might have been expected to come within the remit of this special force. Instead the army was to look to the line regiments for 'intelligent' men who could be trained by the Reverend Gamble.[20]

It was not until the invasion crisis in 1803 that Gamble's knowledge and expertise in communications was again called upon by the Duke of York. In early November, General Craig commanding in Eastern England reported to the Duke's headquarters that the military telegraph line from London to Norwich via Colchester and Diss had been completed.[21] This was probably the telegraph which had been approved in 1798 although reasons for the delay are unclear. A local Norwich source reports that a telegraph on top of the castle also communicated with Yarmouth 24 miles (39Km) away,[22] but the date and the route are unclear. The only intermediate station seems to have been on or near Strumshaw Mill. This also seems to have been a military line for the information of General Milner, whose headquarters was nearby and who would have wanted up-to-date information about enemy intentions from the Admiralty signal post in touch with the naval squadrons resting from blockade duty in Yarmouth roads.

On 7th November Gamble went to Norwich specifically to instruct men on the working of telegraphs which were manned by regimental detachments of an NCO and three men.[23]

No record of the military telegraph to London has survived and the absence of any traces or details of ground being rented suggests that portable telegraphs were used, although there is no confirmation that this was so. The distance covered would have been about 90 miles (145km) so if it did work successfully it would have been quite an achievement. What is also noteworthy is that it was set up long before the Admiralty Shutter telegraph line which also ran from London to Yarmouth. This was proposed in 1801, but not actually built until 1808, and it followed a much different and longer inland route via St Albans, Dunstable and Royston.[24]

It is not surprising that the rush to prepare defences against the French threat in the summer of 1803 overrode the usual slow procedures of the Quarter Master General's Department. An enquiry into military expenditure three years later raised questions about telegraphs and found information hard to come by. Even from the scant evidence presented, it is clear the Commander-in-Chief was responsible for the introduction of the first systems of organised signalling into the early 19th century British army. He wrote to his generals confirming that telegraphs should be set up. He recommended they should use the experienced services of the Reverend Gamble saying: **Mr Gamble is to receive your directions for establishing what you may judge necessary throughout your district.** By which he surely meant that Gamble would decide on the type or method of telegraphing and its route and operation, once the generals told him the objectives they wanted to achieve. The Commission of Enquiry found that work on the telegraphs was carried out by local tradesmen employed by Gamble, although they did not know on what terms.[26]

During these early years signalling by telegraph could mean either mechanical apparatus with shutters or arms, or masts flying flags, balls and pennants. It seems all of these methods were used, the responsibility to decide which, being left to the general of each district. General Craig told the War Office that he regarded all methods of signalling, including beacons, as being the same and that he proposed to pay for them from his budget for field works.[27]

There is little in the records about the methods used on the Kent coast, except that in August 1803 General Morse asked General Dundas for authority to put flag staffs on Shorncliffe Redoubt at Hythe, to communicate with the Admiralty signal post at Folkestone. This was approved, as was a request to have another on Aldington Knoll (near Ashford) to communicate with the military camp there.[28] Even less has survived about Hampshire and the Isle of Wight, although in October 1803 a request was made by the general in charge of the area to be supplied with flags: **in order that he can adopt a code of signals that cannot interfere with those of the Navy.** This request to the Admiralty was rejected because they were issued only for naval service but it suggests that a system of military signals for Portsmouth and the Isle of Wight was being considered.[29] Fortunately much of the detail of the military telegraph set up on the Sussex Coast has survived. In this area Mr Gamble's advice seems not to have been sought nor his radiated telegraph used. Instead, acting on orders from the Duke of York's office, Colonel Smyth surveyed a route of 50 miles (80km) between Winchelsea and Brighton and set up a telegraph line to connect all the defending divisions along the coast. There were signalling and answering stations of a permanent nature linking the headquarters of six generals with that of General Pulteney's district headquarters at Eastbourne. The officer responsible for planning the work seems to have been Sir James Carmichael Smyth, an engineer who had returned to England in 1803 and served on Pulteney's staff as an Assistant Quartermaster General.

Signalling was carried out by hoisting a combination of flags, balls and pennants on tall masts. In his report Colonel Smyth describes his military telegraph as being superior to the Admiralty coast signal posts mentioned in Chapter 2 because: **those posts on the Sussex coast between Fairlight and Beachy Head; the distance of these places being too great for signals to be depended upon.** This was a deficiency in their system with which the Admiralty were well aware, but had done nothing to remedy. The cost of the Smyth telegraph came to £222 and averaged between £40 and £60 a station. At £40 for the cheapest station the design was considered to be adequate for the signals to be seen 12 miles (19km) away. The Sussex telegraph was definitely working by October 1804 and paid for out of General Pulteney's Fieldwork Fund.[30]

The line began at Major General MacKenzie Fraser's headquarters at Winchelsea where nearly 3,000 infantry of the line were camped around Rye, Playden and Silverhill. The next station was at Fairlight above Hastings, where Brigadier General Spencer commanded an army of 2,100 infantry. These were billeted in the surrounding villages of Bexhill, Battle and Hastings.

Another telegraph station was near Bexhill where infantry regiments under General Don were entrenched alongside low cliffs overlooking the sea. That the line passed this way is confirmed by the existence of Telegraph battery (a single 24 pounder gun) marked on an early sketch map of the coast defences.[31]

Further west, General Pulteney the overall commander in Sussex, had his headquarters at Eastbourne. He was also served by two subordinate officers Brigadier Generals Maitland and Lennox and several infantry regiments of 2,700 men. The telegraph station here was actually on Jevington hill overlooking Eastbourne Bay. It seems that from this station there was a telegraph link to the top of Firle Beacon, because in the valley below near Ringmer village there was a depot for brigades of horse artillery. Either direct along the coast from Eastbourne or over the downs from Ringmer the telegraph line continued to a hill near Brighton, where Major General Churchill had his headquarters. Detachments of 1100 men of the 6th and 11th Dragoons were quartered in villages stretching as far apart as Arundel and Lewes. Also in this neighbourhood under subordinate generals with a need to be in contact with General Pulteney were 4500 infantry in county and militia regiments.[32] Some

10 miles (16km) west of Brighton was General Hugonin's headquarters at Worthing and here there were camps for 1150 men of the 1st and 4th Dragoon Guards. Colonel Smyth explains in his report that the telegraph did not extend this far, but he does not give any reason. It may be that the lie of the land was unsuitable, or perhaps his resources had run out.[33]

Part of an old signal book written for officers using the telegraph has survived. It relates directly to General Pulteney's operations in Sussex and gives details of the order in which flags, balls and pennants should be hoisted, so that messages could be spelled out using numbers displayed in nine different positions on the yard arms of a signal mast. Another section of the signal book headed 'General Signals' relates to particular generals and their locations to which messages were to be sent. There is also a special code of signals for urgent messages. These gave the position of the French invasion fleet in the Channel, where it was landing men in Sussex, orders for troop movements, and directions to flood the Sussex and Kent marshes by opening the sluices.[34]

Men were also carefully instructed by officers how to work the telegraphs. These orders probably applied to all military telegraphs in the country at this time. Observations had to be made to the adjacent telegraphs every five minutes. Any negligence was to be punished by loss of jobs and wages. The signallers were cautioned not to divulge the contents of the signal book or messages to anyone other than field officers. When signalling was undertaken, four men had to be present and if messages were being passed up and down the line simultaneously, that from the east took priority. When signals from adjacent posts were not responded to within five minutes a note had to be made in the station journal. Each post had a telescope and this had to be kept dry, cleaned with a dry leather and kept out of sunshine. The flags had to be dried out if wet and the signal balls hung clear of the ground. If there was no wind, stretchers had to be used on the flags.[35]

Men selected for signal duties were paid extra for what was considered to be a technical skill. The NCO got 1/6 and privates 9d per diem. If because of their isolated post they could not be accommodated in barracks they also got 2/- a week for fuel. The men were chosen as signallers because of their intelligence, but if their regiment left the area they went with it and lost their special allowances.[36]

Within a year or two the possibility of a French invasion became much less likely and the regiments that had been mustered in great strength to protect the coast were moved away. The military telegraph set up by Colonel Smyth was either dismantled or taken with them.

The temporary field batteries so hastily constructed in 1803 fell into disuse, although many of the same sites were chosen on which to erect the permanent brick built martello towers. Building the towers began in the Spring of 1805, but it was to be another three or four years before they were finished and armed with one 24 pounder gun each.[37]

Life on the coast was now different and in 1810 a new menace, smuggling, became more of a problem as well as dangerous for those trying to control it. The Treasury was concerned about revenue losses and the upsurge of lawlessness which the smuggling gangs caused. It was, however, unwilling or unable to sanction the building of more guard houses, or pay for perpetual night patrols, and turned to the army detachments watching the coast for help.

Lord Charles Somerset who commanded in Sussex was asked to permit his soldiers manning the martello towers to signal intelligence about smuggling and shipwrecks to assist customs officers.[38] It was a practical and low cost measure in the fight against smuggling and it was also an aid to the defence of the coast. Along the mostly flat coastline between Hythe in Kent and Seaford in Sussex martello towers had replaced the old fieldwork batteries. The towers spaced at 500 yard (457m) intervals were ideal for a line of continuous communication. Somerset saw that he would have the means to pass orders about French raids to the barracks and garrisons where his troops were stationed. He raised no objections to the use of the towers in this way, even though previous attempts to do so had been vetoed, because signalling masts would restrict the traversing of guns through 360° and obstruct fire on their land side. His consent is further proof that the chances of an invasion were now seen as remote. The martello towers built since 1804 at great speed and cost were mostly lying idle and garrisoned only by a few men acting as caretakers.

Orders issued from a regimental headquarters at Winchelsea, (Sussex) explained the procedure. Seven towers including forts Twiss and Moncrieff in Kent, and ten towers in Sussex were chosen as military signal stations. Each was given a garrison of a sergeant and nine men, and had to mount a sentry day and night. The remaining 23 towers on the Kent coast and 47 in Sussex had an NCO and six men. They did not need to mount a sentry, but were expected to watch out for signals as each half hour passed.

To keep signalling simple and minimise mistakes only six flag signals were to be used. Three referred to enemy vessels being sighted, east, west or actually landing on the shore. Three more signified the presence of smugglers, east, west or on the shore. At night a combination of lamp signals passed the same message.

A martello tower stands 34 feet (10m) high above the shore and with the addition of a mast the signal could be spotted a long way off when the weather was reasonably clear. When a signal was hoisted, it was reinforced by a blank shot from a musket every five minutes until acknowledged by the next tower with a sentry.

The Admiralty co-operated with these measures by agreeing to include their own coastal signal posts in the scheme and issuing to the towers three signals used to warn merchant vessels of the presence of privateers.[39] In these uncertain and lawless years the difference between enemy and smuggler was not always apparent. However, a year later the Admiralty had second thoughts because of concern about the confusion which might arise between signals at their signal posts and those at the martello towers.[40] Contemporary correspondence with Lord Somerset shows that they then agreed to the integration of both signal systems for this stretch of the coast. A new and extended list of signals was published. This set out how messages were to be signalled between ships, Admiralty signal posts and the martello towers.[41] These new signals gave information about enemy ships, transports, and the landing of troops; privateers chasing merchant men; and the activities of smugglers and the movement of their cargoes. Five interesting secret signals were issued only to martello tower number 27 which stood east of Rye. They were about the departure of ships carrying gold and money from harbours on the Kent coast.[42]

The new arrangements worked well and there was a levy of 10/6 (51pence) a week paid by the Admiralty when signals were passed on their behalf by the soldiers in the martello towers.

How long this co-operative venture over smuggling between the Admiralty and the military lasted is a matter of doubt, but it probably came to an end when the French war was finally over. Most of the martello towers were being used by the Preventative Service or for other purposes because the War Office removed the guns and carriages in 1817.[43]

Speculation with hindsight is always easy and sometimes revealing. Possibly the army's early experience with signals on the South Coast in 1803 left a lasting memory of its usefulness to generals. During the Peninsular War General Wellington attached special signal units to the headquarters of his divisional commanders. Flags on high masts were used to send messages over long distances between signal stations on hills and mountain tops.[44]

When the war ended the units were disbanded and the War Office showed no further interest in signalling. That is until the Crimean conflict broke out in 1855.

The newly invented electric telegraph which had proved so successful on the railways was then used in a war for the first time.[45] It marked the start of a new era in military communications and spelt the end of the old system with its limitations: **Flags fail at 7 miles; shutters and telegraphs at fifteen.**[46]

## White Lights

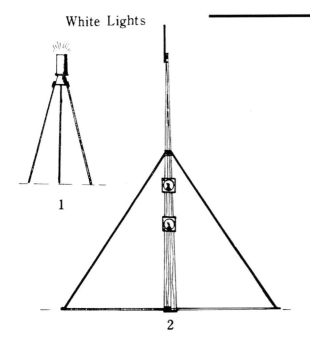

1

2

*37. Methods of signalling at night with white lights and reverbatory lamps were used successfully by Major General William Roy when carrying out his trigonometrical operations.*

*1 A small tripod supporting a box in which a composition to produce a white light, (see text) is burnt. For use on an open hill or church steeple.*

*2 Two reverbatory lamps with 9 inch concave copper reflectors fixed to an ordinary flagstaff.*

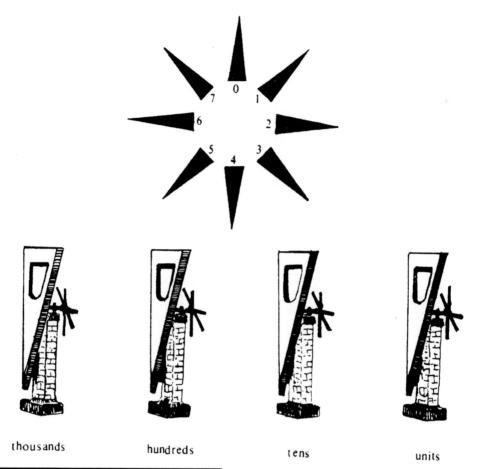

thousands            hundreds            tens            units

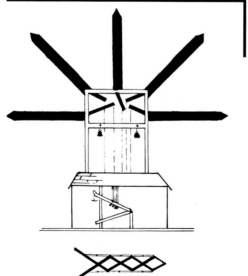

**38. This telegraph invented by Richard Lovell Edgeworth was accepted and then rejected by the Admiralty and the Duke of York. However, a military line did exist for a time in Southern Ireland. The permanent version comprised four towers in a row supporting pointers which could signal combinations of up to eight numbers (0-7). A message was signalled by relating the numbers sent to a large vocabulary of words and phrases.**

**39. The Reverend Gamble's heavy version of his Radiated Telegraph was suitable for building a line of signal stations across country. The arms were covered in black canvas and folded in concertina fashion out of sight when not part of the signal.**

**40. The Reverend Gamble's simplified portable Radiated Telegraph for field use, especially reconnaissance work. It was fixed to a post, tree or building. The five arms unfolded to spell out letters or messages decided by the army commander. The apparatus and a tent for the men was carried in a horse drawn cart.**
**a: all arms open.**
**b: all arms closed.**
**c: the signal.**

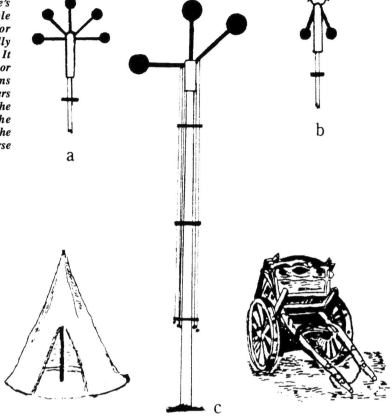

**41. The Reverend Gambles's portable Radiated Telegraph mounted on the roof of the tower of Woolwich Church in 1798.**

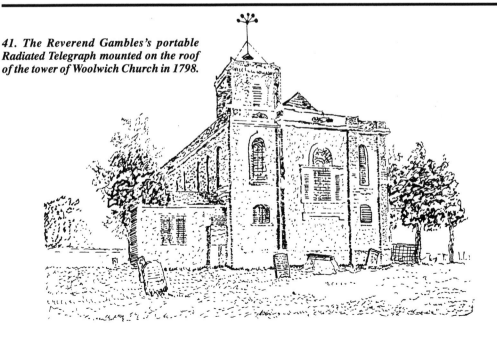

79

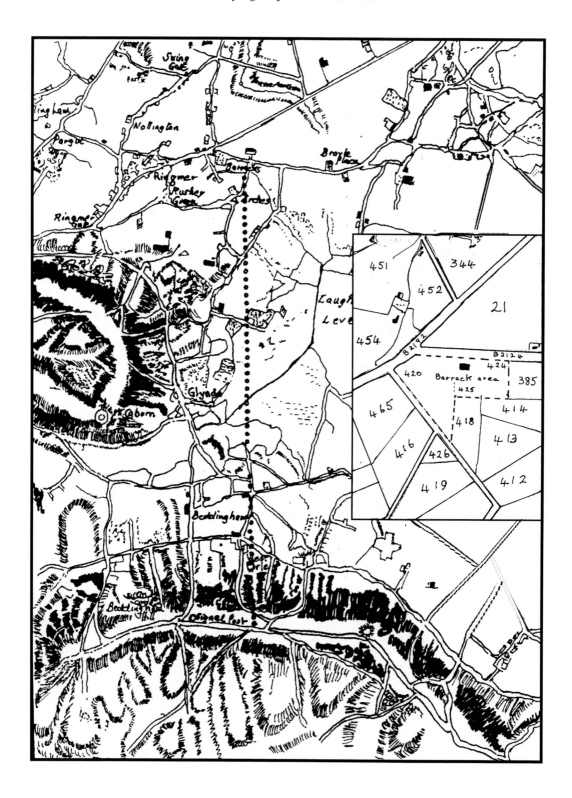

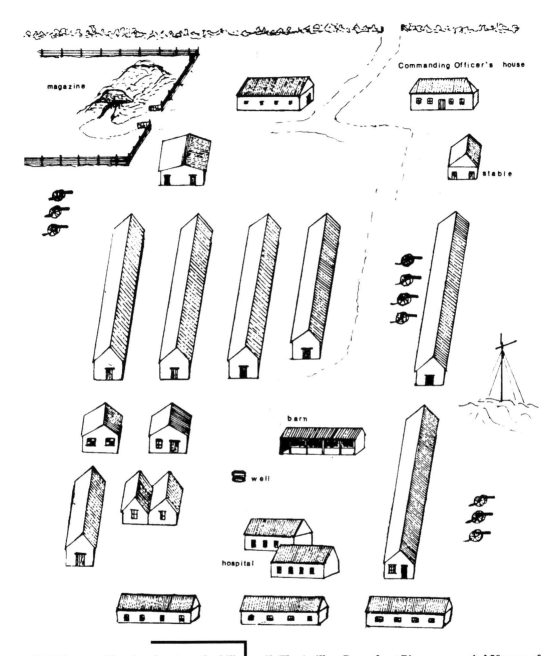

42. Main map: The signal post on the hill above West Firle passed on messages from General Pulteney's Headquarters at Eastbourne, via the Jevington signal post, to the Artillery Barracks near Ringmer. Inset map: The site of the magazine and former artillery barracks shown on the Tithe Award map of 1839-43.

43. The Artillery Barracks at Ringmer occupied 50 acres of land. It was a hutted encampment with tiled roofs, except for the Commanding Officer's house and magazine which were of brick. It was built about 1795 for 276 men and 92 horses. The site was convenient for sending artillery to any part of the coast between Hastings and Littlehampton. 1400 barrels of gun powder were stored in the magazine. The site was sold for other uses about 1827-28.

**44. The route of the Military Telegraph line along the Sussex Coast, built by Lieutenant Colonel Smyth about 1803.**

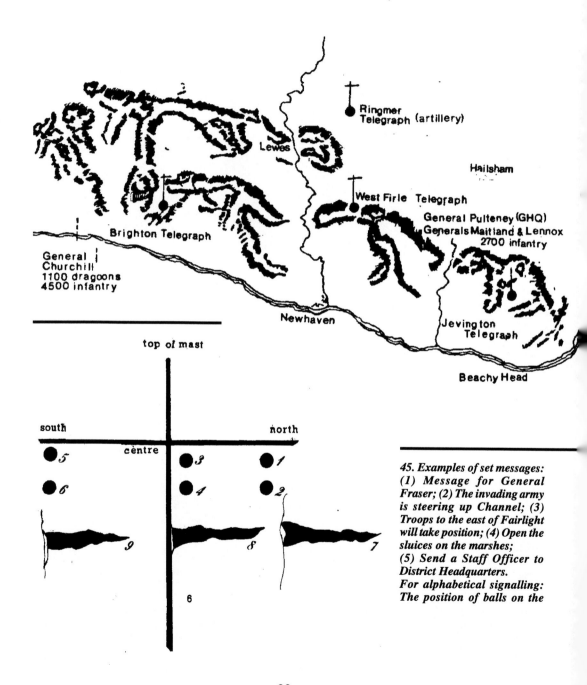

Ringmer Telegraph (artillery)

Lewes

Hailsham

West Firle Telegraph

General Pulteney (GHQ)
Generals Maitland & Lennox
2700 infantry

Brighton Telegraph

General Churchill
1100 dragoons
4500 infantry

Newhaven

Jevington Telegraph

Beachy Head

top of mast

south

north

centre

6

**45. Examples of set messages: (1) Message for General Fraser; (2) The invading army is steering up Channel; (3) Troops to the east of Fairlight will take position; (4) Open the sluices on the marshes; (5) Send a Staff Officer to District Headquarters.**
**For alphabetical signalling: The position of balls on the**

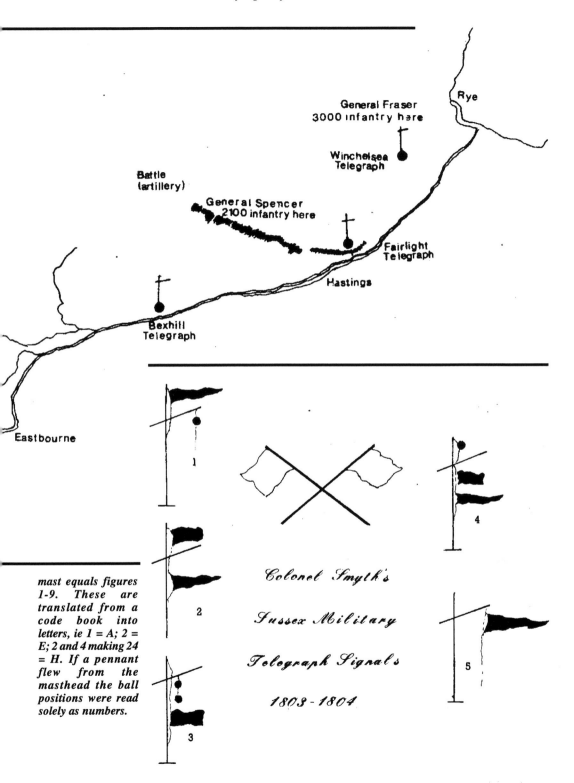

Rye

General Fraser
3000 infantry here

Winchelsea
Telegraph

Battle
(artillery)

General Spencer
2100 infantry here

Fairlight
Telegraph

Hastings

Bexhill
Telegraph

Eastbourne

*mast equals figures 1-9. These are translated from a code book into letters, ie 1 = A; 2 = E; 2 and 4 making 24 = H. If a pennant flew from the masthead the ball positions were read solely as numbers.*

1

2

3

4

5

*Colonel Smyth's*

*Sussex Military*

*Telegraph Signals*

*1803 - 1804*

1

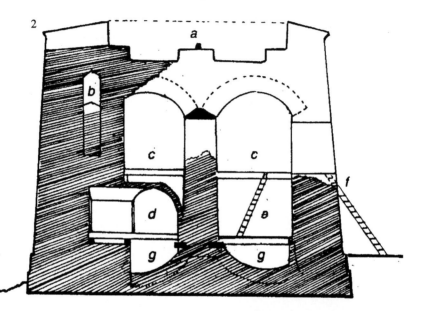

2

3

4

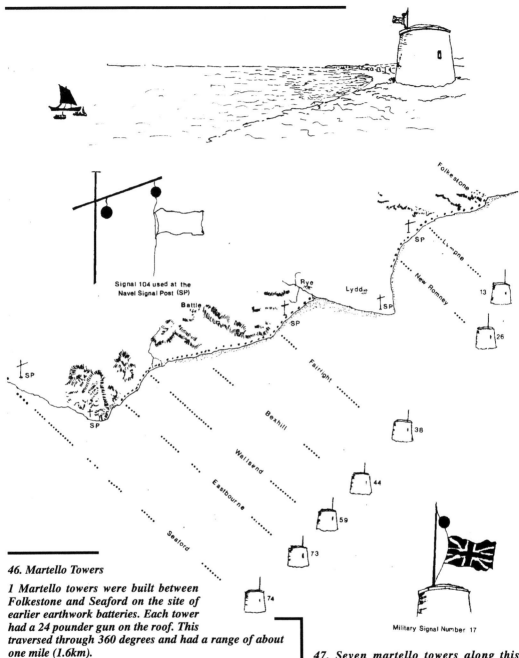

Signal 104 used at the
Navel Signal Post (SP)

Military Signal Number 17

## 46. Martello Towers

*1 Martello towers were built between Folkestone and Seaford on the site of earlier earthwork batteries. Each tower had a 24 pounder gun on the roof. This traverses through 360 degrees and had a range of about one mile (1.6km).*

*2 (a) Gun floor; (b) internal stairs to roof; (c) troop accommodation; (d) magazine; (e) store room; (f) ladder to entrance; (g) Water tanks fed from roof.*

*3 Inside water tank. The slope of the central pillar of the tower can be seen rising on the left.*

*4 Powder barrels in magazine.*

## 47. Seven martello towers along this coastline manned by troops co-operated with the naval signal posts to signal: "Smuggling vessels are at a distance from the shore unloading their cargoes into smaller vessels to be taken ashore." Other signals used by the two services warned about enemy activity at sea.

# CHAPTER 10

## The Inland Shutter Telegraph Routes
## to the Channel Ports

**By this invention the remoteness of distances almost disappear; and all communication of correspondence are effected with the rapidity of the twinkling of an eye.** (Barre August 1794)

How the telegraph first came to be used in Britain is a fascinating story with a hint of mystery which will never be completely resolved because most of the correspondence in the Admiralty 'Promiscuous' files before 1801 was discarded several years later.[1]

Towards the close of the 18th century three clergymen, each working independently, invented and built signalling apparatus which was to advance the sending of messages speedily over long distances. A number of devices for this purpose, some practical others less so, had been proposed during the previous century, but what was different about their acceptance in 1790 was that France and Britain found an invention for long distance communication to be suddenly essential and were prepared to invest money in establishing suitable systems to achieve it. Their haste in embracing what one described as 'this artful contrivance' seems to have been brought about by the upheaval following the French Revolution, and the need to have better communication with armies and navies during the long war in which both countries were engaged. Nicholas Chappe of France was first in the field with what he called a telegraph machine. His device consisted of arms pivoting on a mast similar to what today is known as a semaphore. The French National Convention were so impressed with its possibilities that they financed the building of telegraph stations between Paris and Lille; over a distance of 22 miles (35km)[2] The line took about a year to build and was working by August 1794.

At this point a second clergyman enters the story. He was the Reverend John Gamble, chaplain to the Duke of York, and one of the English contingent sent to the Netherlands the previous year to join the Austrian army fighting the French. In the summer of 1794, while he was at the Duke's headquarters at Berlikum, he saw a plan of the newly built Chappe Telegraph which had been taken from a prisoner of war. A month later, at Grootebrook near Nijmegen, a working model with the code of signals was got for the Duke and sent back to England. As Gamble later explained, the bustle of the campaign gave him no time for experiments and it was not until he returned to England the following January and found that the usefulness of the French telegraph was being so much talked about that he told the Duke about his idea for an improved device. The Duke suggested he review the various alternatives and report back to him. This Gamble did recommending his shutter telegraph which did not work on the semaphore principle of the French machine. Instead it consisted of five boards in a frame which when opened and closed in various combinations formed patterns which could be interpreted as letters and figures.

The Duke paid for Gamble's report to be printed in March 1795, and copies were distributed to politicians and senior naval and military leaders at the Admiralty and Woolwich.[3] The Admiralty seemed very interested and approved payment for him to make experiments between Portsdown Hill at Portsmouth and the Isle of Wight providing the cost did not exceed £150.[4] These took place from June to August, and were inspected by Sir Charles Sexton from the dockyard, and were said to have gone well. When Gamble next approached the Admiralty on 27th August expecting his machine to be adopted, it clearly came as a great shock to him to be told that a broadly similar shutter device designed by another clergyman, Lord George Murray, was to be used for the London to Deal line which was being built shortly.

Lord Murray was an eminent churchman and although that side of his life is well documented, there is little information as to how he came to invent a shutter telegraph machine so similar to that designed by Gamble. The main difference between the two inventions is that the latter's telegraph had five shutters permitting 31 changes of signal whereas Murray's had six allowing for 63 changes. The Admiralty certainly preferred Murray's version because of the greater flexibility of signalling, but as Gamble explained afterwards he could easily have added a sixth shutter. He was also annoyed that having co-operated and having got their support he was dismissed at the last moment with only a casual remark. As he said: **I waited on the Lords of the Admiralty the 27th August 1795, when, in a desultry conversation with one of their Lordship's I was informed, that they had adopted one in preference to that I had offered, and it was invented by Lord George Murray.**[5]

Gamble's report which included most of the known methods of telegraphing information at that time,

86

and his own invention, had received a wide circulation in London. Also a model of his telegraph had been seen by William Pitt the Prime Minister and other dignities earlier that year. As a result Gamble was suspicious that Murray had stolen his design and improved on his invention. He was told by the Admiralty that this was not so as they had viewed a plan of Lord Murray's telegraph the previous year. Gamble was not convinced, but had no evidence to confirm what he clearly thought had happened. However, there is a note in a reliable Admiralty record that Murray had approached them in October 1794 about a proposal for telegraphs between London and Portsmouth so a coincidence of two inventors coming up with an almost identical machine at the same time may well have been true.[6]

With the benefit of hindsight the Admiralty decision to adopt shutter telegraphs instead of the French Chappe telegraph seems flawed, especially as many years later they were to concede that the latter was much superior in poor visibility. Although the Murray shutter telegraph was heavy and cumbersome to work it was cheaper to build and maintain, and made no great demands on the intelligence of the men who operated it. Once it was taken into service the Admiralty saw no point in changing systems especially as they were constantly being bombarded with proposals from other inventors, often suggesting more complicated signalling devices.

The Admiralty having chosen Lord Murray's machine for their first venture in establishing a cross country telegraph paid him £2,000 for his invention in July 1796.[7] Thereafter construction work was soon under way by the Navy Board and the contractors it employed. The Admiralty wanted shutter telegraph lines to run between its London headquarters and the major naval dockyards on the South East coast of England. A contract for surveying the route and building the stations was awarded to George Roebuck, a surveyor, in September and despite the immensity of the task the telegraphs were working within twelve months.[8]

The line to Deal was one of the first to be finished so that messages could be sent to Admiral Peyton responsible for guarding the Narrows of the English Channel and the blockading of the harbours on the French and Flanders coast.[9] Although this command was the only one not associated with a dockyard, the Admiral's cutters and luggers were always to be found anchored in the area of sea known as the 'Downs' off Deal, ready to receive and deliver messages to the shore.

The Deal line also passed close to the naval base at Chatham at the head of the River Medway; and from Beacon Hill near Faversham a spur line was built to the Sheerness dockyard. These anchorages were under the jurisdiction of Admiral Buckner who was responsible for the operations of naval squadrons in most of the North Sea.[10] The third shutter telegraph line which was also ready in 1796 was the one which went from London through Surrey and Sussex to Portsmouth harbour. Its vulnerable position on the South Coast made it the most important of the home commands and the naval squadrons based there were responsible for the protection of the central part of the English Channel.[11]

On 15th April 1796 the Admiralty decided that the sheltered anchorage of Torbay in Devon and the naval harbours of Plymouth and Falmouth should be linked by shutter telegraph to London. They asked for Lord Murray to be consulted on the necessary steps to be taken to do this on the: **best and cheapest terms.** To avoid duplicating the telegraph lines into London he was asked to consider following the Portsmouth telegraph route as far as Haste Hill in Sussex, (in error it was misnamed Hastings Hill) and then on through the western counties to Cornwall.[12] For unexplained reasons this project seems not to have been started until 1805-1806, and although it was then soon completed as far as Plymouth the planned extension to Falmouth was never built. Torbay was also included in their 1796 plans for this route as the sticky mud of its seabed made it ideal for anchoring many ships. As a consequence many naval families lived in the Torbay area. The shutter telegraph route never touched the coast at this point, however, but passed along the hills some miles inland. The only other naval shutter telegraph line built in England was one to Yarmouth which was used as an anchorage by the fleet protecting the North sea. Its route was surveyed much later than the others and it did not begin working until 1808; it was to close along with the others at the end of the war.

From London to Portsmouth, and London to Deal, as the crow flies, the distance differs only slightly and is about 64 and 69 miles (103-111km) respectively. There were seven intermediate shutter stations on the Portsmouth line, eight on that to Deal, with three on a spur to Sheerness. The average distance between stations was about 8 miles (13km), but this was within a range of intervals of three to eleven miles (5-18KM). Generally the shutter telegraph stations were about the same distance apart as the Admiralty signal posts along the coast which suggests that both systems had the same limits of visibility even though different methods of signalling were used.

Very little can be found in official papers about the construction and functioning of the shutter telegraph stations and most of the surviving information comes from journal articles and private sources.[13] Furthermore these accounts often differ although it may be that changes were made over time to improve buildings and performance.[14] Given this uncertainty, what follows is a general description of a shutter telegraph station and how it was used between its establishment in 1796 and close down.

The telegraph signal structure was a strong timber framework 20ft (6m) high, firmly embedded in the ground to resist wind pressure and the movement of the shutters. Six wooden shutters each about 3ft (1m) square were suspended on spindles in three double rows inside the frame. There was a vertical gap in the centre of the frame to allow for the ropes which turned the shutters. This space also made the closed shutters more visible from a distance. The ropes passed down through a hole in the roof of a wooden shack which stood under the frame. Inside the hut the ropes were manipulated by an operator who moved them into one of two positions to make the signal. In the upright or closed position they represented a letter, but when poised horizontally, in an open position they were not in use and so invisible from afar. Inside the hut they were connected to a brake mechanism which locked the shutters, and returned them to the open position when released. Usually three men were needed to staff the station and do what was needed to repeat the signals up and down the line. The absence of any reference to telegraph stations in the Navy List suggests that the staff, unlike that of the coast signal posts did not include an officer.[15] This was economical from the Admiralty viewpoint, and was sensible given that on the coast an officer's analysis of the strength of the enemy and his likely intentions was necessary before hoisting an alarm signal. All the shutter station crew had to do was to pass on the message. As to the men who staffed the stations, there is almost no information as to how they were selected and trained. Although it might be expected that many had a naval or seafaring background this is by no means certain and one source reports a diversity of previous jobs not connected with the sea; labourers, servants and gardeners. Like the signal posts on the coast many of the shutter stations were on isolated hill tops and the Admiralty probably took the best men willing to work there.

The signal men using a telescope, had to watch adjacent stations for a message being transmitted letter by letter and then to haul on the ropes of the shutters to pass it on. In this they were helped by the sending of a preparatory or get ready signal which was passed rapidly along the line to indicate a message was imminent and the direction of travel. Each letter was signalled separately and was not followed by another until its receipt was acknowledged by being repeated at the receiving station. No official code books appear to have survived, but from other sources it is reported that certain groups of letters and abbreviated words were used to refer to ships, commanders and other well used words or phrases in naval jargon. The time it took to pass a message between the terminal stations depended of course on weather conditions and the length of the message. This was kept as short as possible. When visibility was good transmission times were measured in minutes over distances of 50-60 miles (80-96km)[17] It was said that over time the signalmen achieved a high state of speed and accuracy. From the scanty evidence available when all operating conditions were normal most messages were completed within 30 minutes, (one way). In a conversation with some experienced signalmen Sir Richard Phillips was told that on average all day visibilty was good on 200 days, only possible for part of the day on 60 days, and too bad for signalling on the remaining days each year. For those shutter stations close to London performance was often badly affected by drifting smoke from the city chimneys. [18]

From a scrutiny of the weight of correspondence passing between various sections of the Admiralty in London and the naval dockyards it is apparent that most of it went by mail coach or messenger. In December 1805 for example more than 123 letters many with bulky enclosures were signed by Admiral Montague at Portsmouth. In addition there were routine returns, finance lists and schedules of work undertaken or completed by the Navy works department.[19]

The shutter telegraph was reserved for important communications between senior officers. In making its award to Lord Murray for establishing the telegraphs the Privy Council described the system as being: **for the speedy conveyance of orders and information to Flag Officers and Commanders of H.M. Ships.**[20] Thus making it clear that only officers with the rank of Admiral and above were entitled to use it. In orders issued in July 1796 the Admiralty instructed their admirals that they were to use the telegraph: **on occasions of importance and when in need of immediate direction.**[21] The content of messages sent over the telegraph is disclosed in confirmatory letters and in other correspondence between London and the dockyards. These included appointments; promotions, urgent sailing orders for ships' captains, and instructions for warships to get ready for sea.[22] Although much of it was fairly routine administrative traffic, it was about the direction of the naval war at a senior level. Some warlike transmissions referred to the sighting of enemy squadrons sailing from French ports, and the return of the Channel fleet from a patrol.[23] In August 1796 the Admiralty wanted to stop Admiral Blyth, who was known to be off Torbay in **HMS Brunswick**, from sailing near the Western Isles. The line to Plymouth and the coastal signal posts were not then ready and so the order was sent by telegraph to Portsmouth where it was passed on by swift cutter to the Admiral. [24]   The signal posts manned by seamen every few miles along the coast and the shutter telegraph terminals at the principal naval dockyards gave the Admiralty an integrated and rapid (for the age) communication system. The two great advantages were that information about the French or other ship movements could be fed in at any point on the coast and then sent on to the Admiralty. This assisted the Admiralty in its understanding of the strategic situation in the English Channel, enabling it to react quickly in the issue of orders to Admirals and the deployment of their ships. A two way facility confirmed by a mention in letters from the Commander in Chief at Portsmouth: **I have sent notice of the sailing of the Brest (French) fleet to the west by coast signals,** and : **I learn by coast signals that the Channel Fleet has sailed from Torbay.**[25] As Chapter 9 explains there was also liaison, perhaps not always without difficulties, between the Admiralty network of telegraphs and coast signals and the army generals commanding troops along the shore.

The shutter telegraph first set up in 1796 was finally closed down shortly after the defeat of Napoleon. The exact date in uncertain, but the line was never operational after March 1816.[26] By this time the telegraph lines had been in constant use for twenty years, the shutter machines were well worn, and the buildings delapidated and in a poor state. The Admiralty's intention was to replace the system with semaphore machines.    These had proved successful on the coast and in experiments in Kent. However, these plans were for the future and it was to be many years before they could be realised.

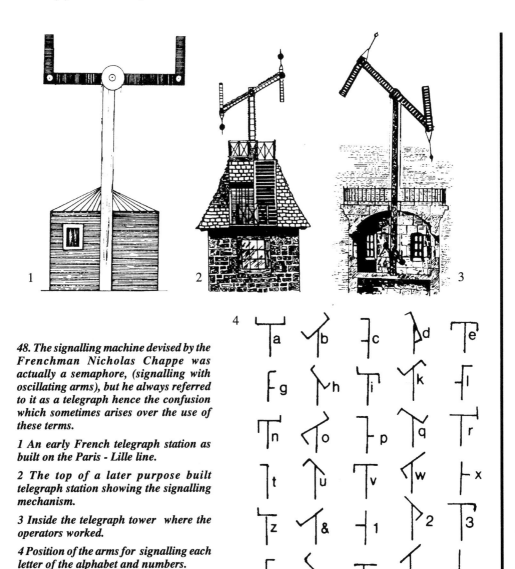

*48. The signalling machine devised by the Frenchman Nicholas Chappe was actually a semaphore, (signalling with oscillating arms), but he always referred to it as a telegraph hence the confusion which sometimes arises over the use of these terms.*

*1 An early French telegraph station as built on the Paris - Lille line.*

*2 The top of a later purpose built telegraph station showing the signalling mechanism.*

*3 Inside the telegraph tower  where the operators worked.*

*4 Position of the arms for  signalling each letter of the alphabet and numbers.*

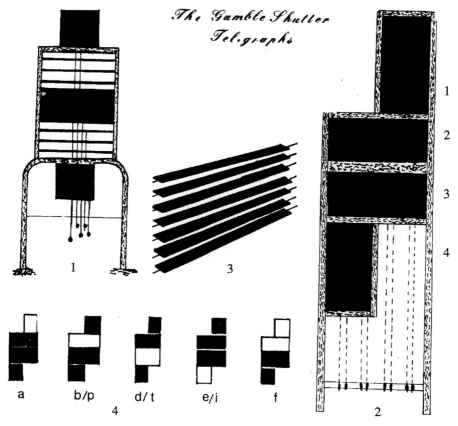

*The Gamble Shutter Telegraphs*

**49. The Reverend John Gamble designed two versions of his shutter telegraph. Both were rejected by the Admiralty who preferred the machine invented by Lord George Murray.**

*1 Five boards, each of three leaves set in a huge frame fashioned from ships topmasts. A hut for the operatives was built beneath.*

*2 Worked similarly, but with four boards, each of seven leaves. This model underwent successful trials between Portsdown Hill and Portsmouth town. It used a phonetic alphabet of 15 letters.*

*3 Closed boards Fig 2 (2 and 3) in an open position.*

*4 Signals for part of the alphabet used by the machine in Fig.2.*

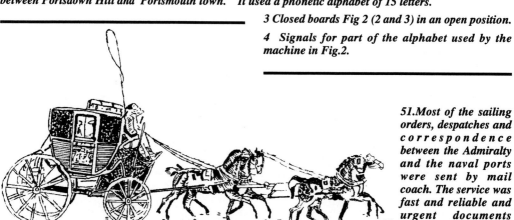

*51.Most of the sailing orders, despatches and correspondence between the Admiralty and the naval ports were sent by mail coach. The service was fast and reliable and urgent documents travelled in Express coaches.*

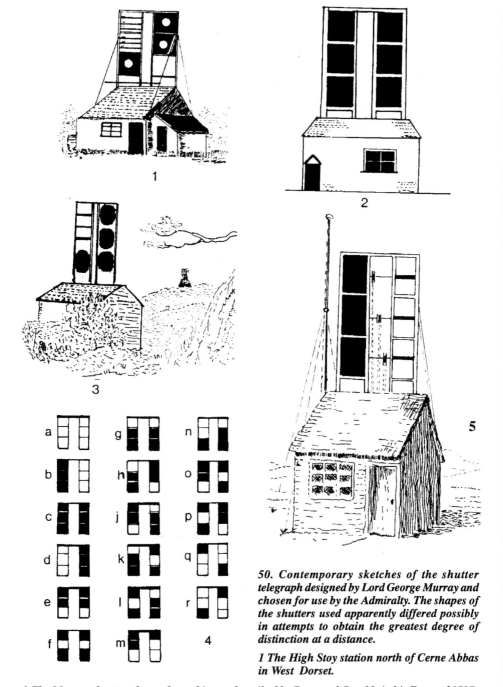

**50. Contemporary sketches of the shutter telegraph designed by Lord George Murray and chosen for use by the Admiralty. The shapes of the shutters used apparently differed possibly in attempts to obtain the greatest degree of distinction at a distance.**

*1 The High Stoy station north of Cerne Abbas in West Dorset.*

*2 The Murray shutter telegraph machine as described by Reverend Gamble in his Essay of 1797.*

*3 A shutter telegraph station in Kent.*

*4 Part of the alphabetic pattern of signals. The (closed) black shutters denote the letter.*

*5 The New Cross station in 1796.*

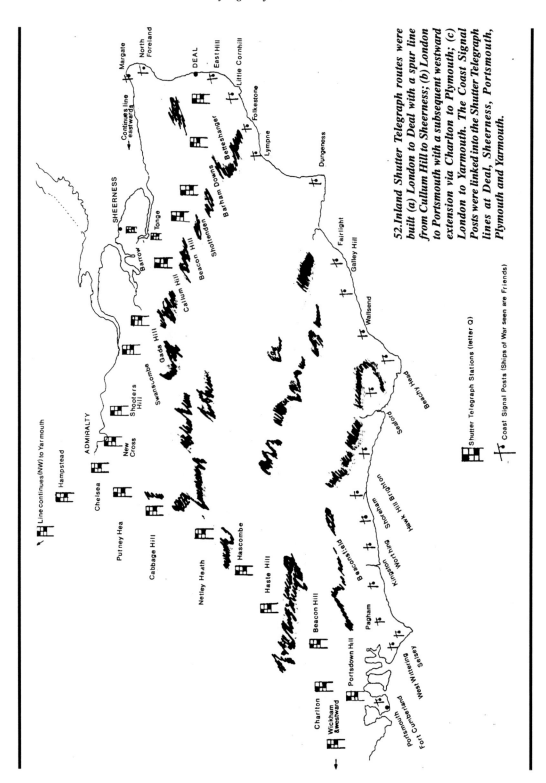

52. *Inland Shutter Telegraph routes were built (a) London to Deal with a spur line from Cullum Hill to Sheerness; (b) London to Portsmouth with a subsequent westward extension via Charlton to Plymouth; (c) London to Yarmouth. The Coast Signal Posts were linked into the Shutter Telegraph lines at Deal, Sheerness, Portsmouth, Plymouth and Yarmouth.*

Margate
North Foreland
DEAL
East Hill
Little Cornhill
Folkestone
Betteshanger
Barham Downs
Lympne
Dungeness
Continues line eastwards
SHEERNESS
Tonge
Barrow
Shottenden
Beacon Hill
Cullum Hill
Fairlight
Galley Hill
Gads Hill
Wallsend
Shooters Hill
ADMIRALTY
Swanscombe
New Cross
Beachy Head
Seabrook
Chelsea
Putney Hea
Cabbage Hill
Netley Heath
Hascombe
Brighton
Hawk Hill
Worthing
Shoreham
Kingston
Beaconsfield
Haste Hill
Line continues (NW) to Yarmouth
Hampstead
Pagham
Beacon Hill
Portsdown Hill
Selsey
West Wittering
Fort Cumberland
Portsmouth
Charlton
Wickham & westward

Shutter Telegraph Stations (letter Q)

Coast Signal Posts (Ships of War seen are Friends)

# CHAPTER 11

## Semaphores on the South Coast -
## An Admiralty 'White Elephant'

Commodore William Owen in His Majesty's ship **Clyde** was cruising off the French coast in the summer of 1806 with orders to examine the shore between Calais and Etaples and report any unusual occurrence. As well as changes to the fortifications protecting Boulogne, he found something more significant which he wrote about that day to his admiral, Lord Keith. He said that along this coast, the French had replaced each signal post using flags and balls with a new device. He drew a sketch of a high pole fitted with three arms and noted that each arm could be moved to six different angles enabling it to make nearly 400 signals.[1] We now know that this new coastal semaphore was invented some years earlier by a French artillery officer, although it seems not to have been reported in English journals until Captain Pasley of the Royal Engineers mentioned it in 1810, claiming it was first seen on the Flanders coastline about the time of Commodore Owen's report.[2]

Although the superiority of the clearness of semaphore signals over other signalling methods was already acknowledged by some naval officers the Admiralty were reluctant to make any changes. Apart from the cost of changing, the ball and flag method was effective when weather conditions made signalling possible. Likewise the cumbersome Murray shutter telegraph lines across the hills between London and the Channel ports met their needs adequately most of the time. Change, however, could not be entirely resisted and it was the army who took the lead. In 1809, Generals Don and Doyle in the Channel Islands, pressed for a French type semaphore to be set up on each of the four Channel Islands to communicate with each other and naval ships blockading the French coast. The Admiralty co-operated over the negotiations which lasted a year. Apparently a new comparison of the costs and benefits influenced the outcome.[3] There seems to have been a change in Admiralty thinking about this time, for money was also set aside to experiment with the French coastal semaphore between Sheerness, the Nore and Horsley Bay on the East coast. This was estimated to cost £1745.[4] The route was eventually decided using many of the old signal stations most of which were converted by the end of 1811 or soon after.[5] We know that in November, Admiral Young commanding in the Downs, was told that existing coast signal posts in Essex using flags and balls were to be converted to what the Admiralty then described as 'Semaphores or Pole Telegraphs'.[6] It seems that despite their original resistance to what was in effect a modernising of the coast signals, the Admiralty had accepted the superiority of semaphore signalling for in 1812 they confirmed their intention to extend the conversion of stations on the East Coast, from Ordford river to Yarmouth, and south from Sheerness to Deal in Kent.[7] They also had plans to continue the conversion into Sussex and beyond, but it soon became apparent that new surveys of this route were needed first.[8] This was because some stations were poorly sited with buildings unsuitable for the installation of machinery to work the semaphores. Extra stations were also needed in Sussex to improve visibility lines in places where there had been difficulties over the sending of ball and flag signals for years. A further complication was reluctance by some landowners to agree reasonable terms for using their land. It was also necessary to seek the approval of the Ordnance for semaphores to be erected on Sandown Castle and other forts and batteries on the Kent coast.

The French pattern semaphore first used on the English coast had three arms fixed to a 35 foot (11metre) high mast, the bottom 5 feet (2 metre) of which was sunk below the roof of the signal house. Here the men worked the three dials by which the arms were pulled by rods into different positions to spell out the letter or word being sent. These machines were manufactured by Henry Maudslay at his London works.[9] It is clear from an examination of the voluminous correspondence between the Admiralty and the Navy Board, who were continually being told to get on with the job, that between 1811 and 1814, because of delays in the conversion work, some stations in Essex and Kent were using the ball and flag method and others the new semaphore machines.

Once they were satisfied with the working of the semaphores on the East Coast, the Admiralty decided to convert all the ball and flag stations from Kent to Lands End in Cornwall.[10] A decision which was inevitable, given the impossibility of expecting two different systems on the same coastline to work without mistakes and confusion. Unfortunately this optimistic intention was bedevilled by political events and consequential uncertainty at the Admiralty. The defeat of Napoleon, his subsequent comeback, and then his final defeat at Waterloo in 1815, led to calls to reduce the naval budget, which in turn led to doubts as to whether there was really any need for a coastwise signalling system in peacetime. If it was to be kept up in case of a future war, to what use was it to be put meanwhile and which government department was to pay for it? It should be remembered that twice, the coast signals had been closed down and re-established at some cost when war began again. The experience was so recent that unsurprisingly there was doubt as to whether the peace would hold.

The Admiralty referred the future of the coast signals to the Treasury for their advice and, mindful of the cost, suggested that during peacetime semaphore stations could be useful in the prevention of smuggling. But the Treasury thought otherwise and implied that if the Admiralty set them up they would have to decide how they should be paid for within their budget. As to their usefulness to the Customs and Revenue services, their view was that smugglers would soon become familiar with the messages being passed by the semaphores which would limit their value.[11] This despite rising concern generally about an increase in the boldness of smugglers. Thomas Reid in charge of the Kingston (Sussex) signal post reported that local smugglers were building their own signal station a mile from his to signal to French boats offshore![12]

The outcome for some months was that the Navy Board was left with the difficult job of reconciling one Admiralty decision to dispose of the old line of signal posts with that of another to retain some of them for the operation of a semaphore system whose use and route had not then been determined. The difficulty was further complicated because no one knew which existing sites and buildings were suitable for retention. There was general agreement, however, that new surveys of the Kent and Sussex routes were needed before any work could begin.

The Admiralty decided on a compromise and ordered the discharge of all the officers and men staffing the signal posts only a few of which had semaphores. This immediately reduced the manpower costs. Those officers who wanted to remain in the signal houses which had become their homes could do so although they would not receive any pay. The Navy Board continued to meet the cost of repairs to the signal houses so as to keep them in good condition. If these were in an exposed position, or distant from a village, there was to be an inducement for officers to remain, by the offer of coal allowance for heating.[13]

Although this decision put an end to the uncertainty, no progress in building the South Coast semaphore line was made throughout 1815. In June a general order was issued for the final disposal of all the old ball and flag signal houses. Only some were to be kept if they were likely to be on the route for a new semaphore line to Cornwall.[14]

Those in charge at the Admiralty were also undecided about whether the three arm semaphore was the most suitable machine for their needs and the Navy Board were told not to place any more orders until this matter was resolved. Their doubts arose because Sir Home Popham (author of the successful Telegraphic Signal code) had sent them a design for a similar semaphore, but with only two arms. A trial with this machine on a temporary route between London and Chatham was successful and led to orders that these were to be used in future. The French three arm machines already in use on the East Coast and those ordered for Kent and Sussex were to be withdrawn and stored.[15]

Unwilling to be caught unawares if there was a fresh emergency, the Admiralty then went ahead to make a new survey of the southern coastline of England. Mr Thomas Goddard who had previously been the purser on board the Royal Sovereign was chosen to undertake this task. His special qualifications for this task are not mentioned, but his skills as a master mariner in navigation and signalling were probably excellent. He began by surveying the best sites for semaphore stations on the coast between Kent and the Isle of Wight.[16] Working in close association with him was Mr Thomas Edgecombe, the master house carpenter from the Sheerness Naval Yard. His task was to inspect the signal houses to see whether the new semaphore machinery could be installed.[17] Goddard was much in demand at this time for he was also under orders to survey the much longer cross country routes from London to Portsmouth and Deal. Inevitably delays ensued. It was not until 1816 that Goddard was able to report on the best route for the new coast semaphore line to follow and recommend which signal houses were suitable for conversion. During this survey he was also asked by the Admiralty to experiment with a portable semaphore apparatus for use instead of permanent buildings between Kent and Cornwall. For this trial he used locations at or close to the old ball and flag signal posts.[18] He also seems to have suspected whether there was any real commitment by the Admiralty to finance the building and manning of a line of permanent stations as far as Land's End. The experiment with the portable apparatus was successful and he wrote accordingly to the Admiralty. As a result it was decided not to continue the coast line to Cornwall and no permanent semaphore stations were built westward after Beachy Head.[19] With the fieldwork survey for the South Coast completed the project was still hampered by doubts as to what use could be made of the line when it was built. Enquiries to the port admirals at Sheerness, Portsmouth and Plymouth as late as 1817, as to whether it would be helpful for their cruisers, if semaphore stations were sited on headlands shows that there were still those in the Admiralty keen to build coast semaphores. However, this approach resulted in a lukewarm and inconclusive response which put an end to this suggestion.[20] From time to time there was renewed interest about the value of a system of coast signals to inform about the activities of smugglers. The Admiralty remained unenthusiastic and warned the Treasury that the revival of the signal stations, discontinued as being useless to the Revenue Service, would be expensive although subsequently this view was to change.[21]

In the summer of 1818 there were new developments. The peace with France was now firmly established, coast defence was no longer a priority and serious efforts were being made to combat smuggling and the loss of revenue to the Treasury. The Coast Blockade Service, commanded by an energetic naval officer Captain Joseph McCulloch, had been set up after 1815. It was having some success and two years later it became the responsibility of the Admiralty to administer. As a semi-military force of armed men operating on shore and at sea, the territory it was responsible for initially was from the North Foreland to Dungeness. Later the area was widened to include Seaford in Sussex. The men were housed in watch houses, many of which were old signal houses or martello towers.[22] Gradually the view gained ground that semaphore communication would help the work of the Coast Blockade.

The picture which emerges during the post war years of attempts to establish a line of semaphore stations on the South Coast is one of long delays and difficulties at all levels. In the Admiralty there was a lack of money and, at times, commitment. The Navy Board responsible for carrying out the work had problems over deciding the best route and negotiating tenancies with obstinate landowners. There were many changes in the sites selected for semaphore stations resulting from the need to get the best visibility for signalling. There was also a good deal of rebuilding and refurbishing of the old signal houses needed. Between 1811 and 1819, some stations between Deal and Beachy Head may have had their buildings ready for the new two arm machines, but it was not until 1820 that any semaphore working was possible.[23] All the available evidence points to the Kent and Sussex coast semaphore line being completed piecemeal; difficulties with landowners over sites and the rents being asked causing long standing hold-ups. This despite the passing of an Act, which empowered the government to acquire land for signal and telegraph stations and to order any obstructions such as trees or buildings, to be removed.[24] Thus none of the South Coast semaphores appear to have begun working until at least five years after the war with France ended. Plans to modernize the signal stations which had given such useful wartime service foundered because they were no longer necessary. In 1819, unable to justify their use to defend the country, the Admiralty agreed that the semaphore stations then nearing completion should be used as an auxiliary measure to help the Coast Blockade service in the prevention of smuggling.[25] It was hoped that by relaying information about the movements of smugglers and their craft between the ships and watch houses of the Coast Blockade, Captain McCulloch's drive to suppress smuggling would be helped. However, the success of this venture was limited for the semaphore stations were only to have a working life of six years. Perhaps this is not so surprising because most of the smuggling action took place at night. In none of the many contemporary accounts and reports of the activities of the Customs and the Coast Blockade has any credit been given, so far as is known, to the usefulness of the semaphores to this service.[26] The system probably never lived up to expectations, for within a few years some of the signal houses were said to be unfit for use. The machinery was broken or left unrepaired and there were general shortages of equipment. Captain Mingaye in charge of the Coast Blockade ship, **Iberium**, told the Admiralty that he did not consider the semaphores useful to his work and did not need any more staff to operate them.[27] It was perhaps a disadvantage that the semaphore line only went as far as Beachy Head, whereas there was a lot of smuggling activity along the rest of the Sussex coast westwards. There was a proposal to extend it as far as Chichester, but this would have meant building another seventeen stations. Offers from Brighton and Seaford builders to construct these extra stations at a similar cost to the one at Beachy Head were received in 1826, but these were never built.[28] It is clear that the original objective of the Admiralty to establish a continuous line of semaphore stations along the South Coast between the naval ports was never met. Passing over responsibility for those stations which were completed to the Coast Blockade made the best use of the considerable sum of money already spent. As it happened the Coast Blockade service itself was not to last much longer and was disbanded in 1831.[29]

## State of the Kent and Sussex Naval Semaphore Line in 1820

### KENT

| | |
|---|---|
| Deal (on seafront) | Not yet built |
| Little Cornhill, South Foreland | Awaiting semaphore |
| East Hill, near St Margarets | Not yet built |
| Houghton Court, Capel le Ferne | Ready to operate |
| Martello Tower 4, Folkestone | Not yet ready |
| Fort Moncrieff, Hythe | Not yet ready |
| Martello Tower 27 Globsden Gut | Not yet built |
| Battery No 2, Dungeness | Ready to operate |
| Dungeness Redoubt | Awaiting semaphore |

95

**SUSSEX**

| | |
|---|---|
| Jews Gut, East of Camber | Not yet ready |
| Fairlight | Ready to operate |
| Martello Tower 31, Bexhill | Ready to operate |
| Kewhurst, Little Common | Ready to operate |
| Martello Tower 55, Norman's Bay | Ready to operate |
| Langney Fort, Pevensey Bay | Ready to operate |
| Beachy Head, Eastbourne | Ready to operate |

No further semaphore stations along this coastline west of Beachy Head were ever built.

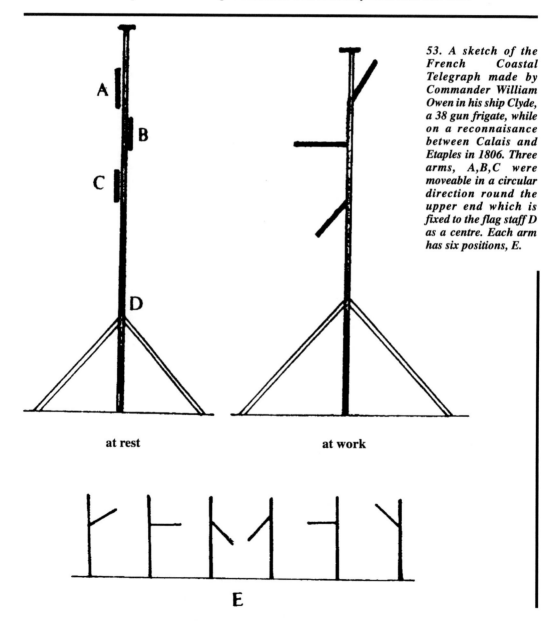

at rest                    at work

*53. A sketch of the French Coastal Telegraph made by Commander William Owen in his ship Clyde, a 38 gun frigate, while on a reconnaisance between Calais and Etaples in 1806. Three arms, A,B,C were moveable in a circular direction round the upper end which is fixed to the flag staff D as a centre. Each arm has six positions, E.*

96

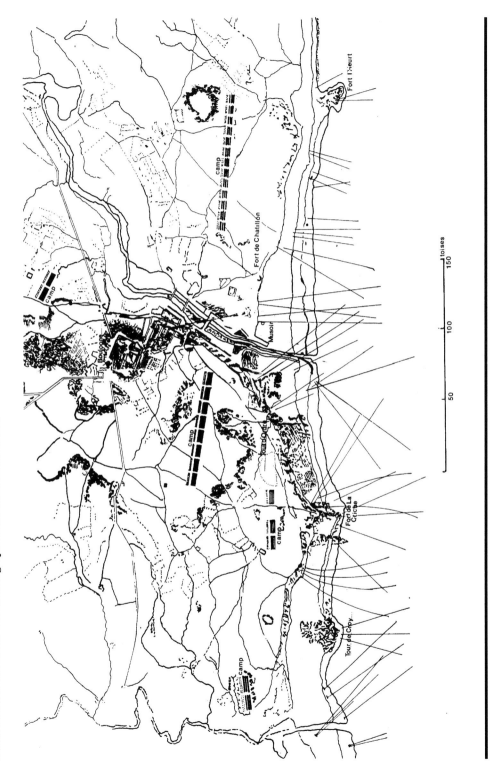

54. The military encampments; and forts and batteries showing their range and fields of fire around the port of Boulogne reported on by Commander Owen when he saw a new French telegraph installation on the coast.

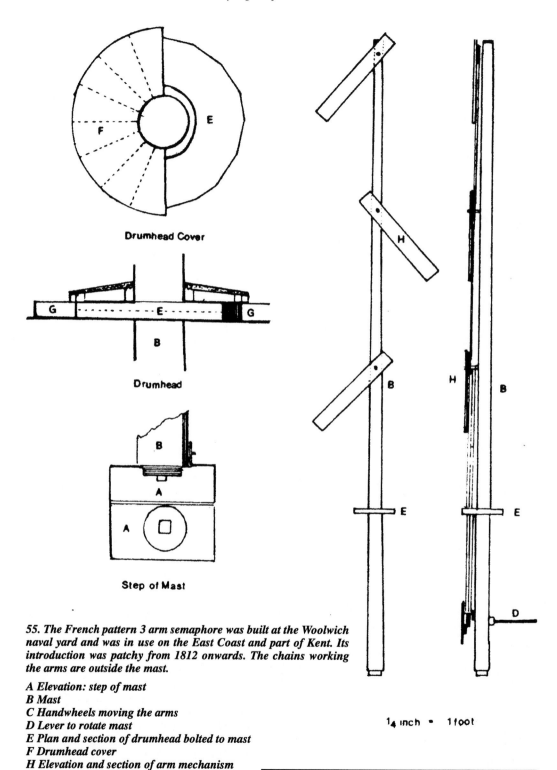

**Drumhead Cover**

**Drumhead**

**Step of Mast**

*55. The French pattern 3 arm semaphore was built at the Woolwich naval yard and was in use on the East Coast and part of Kent. Its introduction was patchy from 1812 onwards. The chains working the arms are outside the mast.*

*A Elevation: step of mast*
*B Mast*
*C Handwheels moving the arms*
*D Lever to rotate mast*
*E Plan and section of drumhead bolted to mast*
*F Drumhead cover*
*H Elevation and section of arm mechanism*

1¼ inch = 1 foot

**56.Plans from the Ministry of Defence Library for the two arm land semaphore based on the one designed by Sir Home Popham. This new machine replaced the three arm French semaphore along the South Coast when the stations were ready to use it between 1811-1819.**

**57. The elevation of a temporary signal house for erection on the South Coast to be fitted with a two arm semaphore machine designed on Sir Home Popham's principles.**

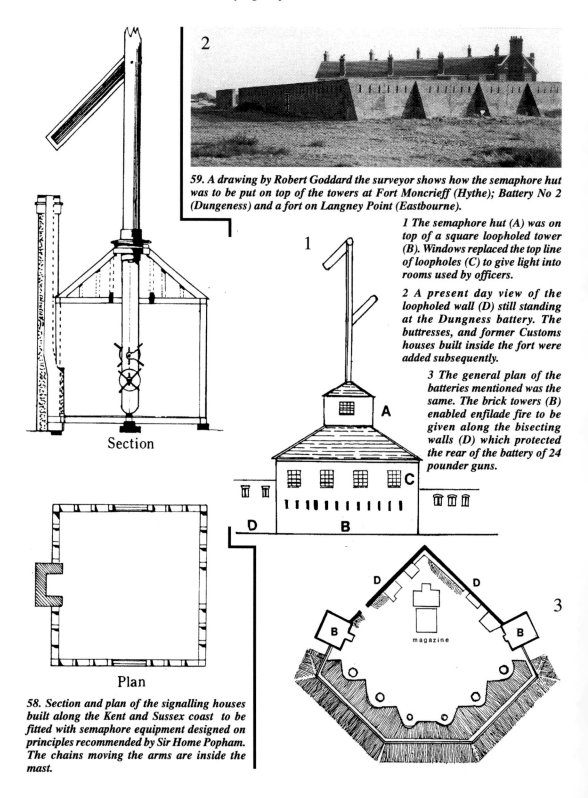

59. *A drawing by Robert Goddard the surveyor shows how the semaphore hut was to be put on top of the towers at Fort Moncrieff (Hythe); Battery No 2 (Dungeness) and a fort on Langney Point (Eastbourne).*

Section

Plan

58. *Section and plan of the signalling houses built along the Kent and Sussex coast to be fitted with semaphore equipment designed on principles recommended by Sir Home Popham. The chains moving the arms are inside the mast.*

1 *The semaphore hut (A) was on top of a square loopholed tower (B). Windows replaced the top line of loopholes (C) to give light into rooms used by officers.*

2 *A present day view of the loopholed wall (D) still standing at the Dungness battery. The buttresses, and former Customs houses built inside the fort were added subsequently.*

3 *The general plan of the batteries mentioned was the same. The brick towers (B) enabled enfilade fire to be given along the bisecting walls (D) which protected the rear of the battery of 24 pounder guns.*

magazine

# CHAPTER 12

# From Admiralty Semaphores to Railway Telegraphs

The Admiralty closed down all its Shutter Telegraph lines to the naval dockyards in March 1816.[1] As with the end of all wars the need to reduce expenditure was paramount. Moreover those in charge of the telegraphs were not blind to its limitations. Some of the stations were not well sited, especially when visibility was poor, and the expanding size of London with smoke from its many chimney's made it even more difficult to see the shutters clearly over a long distance. A question mark also hung over what the future role of an Admiralty communication system across country was to be, whether it was worth the expense, and what method of signalling should be used. Many ideas were received from inventors anxious for their own devices to be given a fair trial, but these were rejected as impractical or having no particular advantage. Eventually the Admiralty decided that a land semaphore machine, (developed from a sea version for ships) and designed by a naval officer Sir Home Riggs Popham, was the best replacement for the old shutter telegraph. It had found favour with naval officers who had experience of other systems, had worked well on an experimental line opened in July 1816 between the Admiralty and Chatham and was being installed along the South Coast.[2] All concerned with this issue were satisfied that viewed from a distance with the naked eye two semaphore arms could be seen much clearer than the old shutters. A cynic might say that the French had come to this decision many years earlier.

Mr Thomas Goddard, the purser of the Royal George (see Chapter 11) was asked to survey and report on the best route for a semaphore line to Portsmouth.[3] At about the same time he was also expected to complete a similar survey for building a new semaphore communication along the Kent and Sussex coast. Over burdened with these jobs it is no wonder completion was to take some time. There were also delays at the Admiralty partly arising from shortage of funds and consequential lack of commitment. Factors which explain the long four year gap between the closing down of the Portsmouth shutter line and the decision to start work on its replacement.

Early on Goddard found the sites and condition of most of the existing shutter buildings unsuitable for his purpose. This led to a search for new sites. In his reports he mentions how he and his workers scrambled through bushes to the top of high hills to peer through a telescope at the next possible site for a semaphore building. He had to juggle with difficult landowners, and places where he wanted to build his semaphores, but which were found to be unsuitable because trees or high ground in the background would obscure the outline of the semaphore arms. The best entry route into London also gave rise to lengthy discussions and so it was not until February 1820 that he was able to present his recommendations and ask the Admiralty which of a choice of routes they would like him to follow.[4]

Goddard's eventual route to Portsmouth with 15 semaphores instead of 9 shutter stations took a wider sweep to the westward after Cooper's hill, (Hinchley Wood, Surrey) until it rejoined the old shutter line near Haste hill in Sussex. The average distance between stations was just under five miles (8km), rather less than previously. The Admiralty finally gave their approval for work to begin in December 1820, and by the following April all the sites had been secured at an average price of £47.20 each although the range was £20-120. It was, however, to be a further two years before the semaphore apparatus was in place and the line was able to pass its first message.[5]

One casualty of the Portsmouth line was the close down of the semaphore route to Chatham. To save expense its machines were dismantled and transferred to the newly built semaphore houses across Surrey and Sussex.[6]

Although some progress was to be made in 1821 on constructing a separate line to Plymouth, which was to branch off from the Portsmouth route at Beacon hill (Sussex), this eventually came to nothing.[7] A few stations were completed, but work stopped after Woodford Green, Downton in Hampshire. It was never resumed; a victim of increasing costs, lack of funds, and obsolescence when the electric telegraph seemed likely to become a reality.

From the outset it had been decided that the semaphore machinery was to be housed in permanent brick buildings with proper living accommodation for the operators. A far cry from the draughty wooden huts put up hastily and cheaply for the shutter stations. The buildings were sited and designed to give maximum visibility to the semaphore masts. Most of the stations on high ground were single storey houses with slate roofs. There were several rooms, one being set aside for semaphore operations. On flatter sites, or in well wooded locations higher buildings were needed. At Cooper's Hill a three storey square tower house was built and at Chatley Heath a massive five storey octagonal tower. On top of Pewley Hill near Guildford there was a house with three floors. To keep out intruders and animals, the country stations were surrounded by ditches, quickset hedges or earthen banks. The semaphore at the London end was worked from a hut high on the roof of the Chelsea Hospital. At Portsmouth several changes of location were made over the years until finally an imposing purpose built semaphore tower was put on the roof of the Port Admiral's Office in 1833,[8] which is still there today. The semaphore mast designed by Sir Home Riggs Popham was a substantial affair extending 30ft (9m) above the top of the accommodation building. It was built from 10 inch (254mm) fir boards bound with iron bands into a tight hexagonal shape so that its internal diameter of 20 inches (508mm) could accommodate the chains and rods for moving the arms. There were two arms each 8ft (2m) long and 15 inches (1.3m) wide. One was fastened at the top of the mast, the other 12ft (3.6m) above the level of the roof. When the arms were at rest they folded inside the mast. At the base of the mast, in the operating room, a gear mechanism with two winch handles enabled the men to swing the arms into 48 different patterns to signal letters and figures. The Popham Vocabulary Code as it was known was in use until the Portsmouth line closed for ever in 1850.[9] The London and Portsmouth termini were staffed with a crew of three, but at the intermediate stations there was only an officer and one assistant, usually an old seaman with a reputation as good lookout or 'glass man'.

By previous standards the accommodation was spacious and there was room for the officer's family, and sometimes that of his assistant as well.

As with the shutter telegraph it replaced the semaphore line was reserved for the use of senior naval officers; a jealously guarded privilege. As the war with France was long over it seems to have been less used than hitherto. One study confirms that business about the operation of the dockyard was seldom sent by the semaphore.[10] This went by mailcoach or courier. At one stage there was even a suggestion that the semaphore line should be used by the public to send commercial messages. Although this was not acted upon it does suggest that there may have been fewer official messages, and this must have raised questions about the economics of keeping the line open.

Its fate, however, was to be finally settled by two technological advances, the steam railway and the electric telegraph. Both played an important complementary role in the Admiralty's adoption of a new system of communication, and how this came about needs some explanation.

First the railway. The piecemeal, but gradual spread of the rail network throughout England during the second quarter of the 19th century took place as investors seeking profits raised funds and formed companies to build new lines. South of the London metropolitan area, the London & Southampton Railway was completed on 11th May 1840.[11] With an eye to future expansion it had shrewdly changed its name to the London & South Western Railway and asked Parliament to approve Bills for additional lines, to Portsmouth and Gosport. Royal assent for these was given in June 1839.[12] Under this legislation only a line to Gosport was actually built at this time. It may seem strange that Gosport was chosen instead of Portsmouth, but there were doubts about the wisdom of making any gaps in the fortified Hilsea Lines which protected the town from a French army invasion on the coast west of Littlehampton.[13]

The route to Gosport branched off from the main Southampton line at Bishopstoke which was then a station in open country about one mile from the village. It was renamed Eastleigh when the town and railway works developed around it. The line then passed through Botley and Fareham, although it was not opened for passengers until February 1842 due to problems with a tunnel at Fareham.[14]

The significance of the Gosport railway in the history of naval communications is that it was along its trackside that the first electric telegraph communication for the use of the Admiralty was built. At this point an account of how the electric telegraph was developed and came to be associated with railway working will be helpful. From the 18th century onwards many inventors in Britain and Europe were experimenting to discover what was then known about electricity to transmit messages along a wire.

In July 1816 Francis Ronalds, a young London businessman and scientist had offered his version of a working electric telegraph to Lord Melville, First Lord of the Admiralty. This offer was rejected with a curt note. Influential secretary Sir John Barrow replying: **that telegraphs of any kind are now wholly unnecessary and that no other than those in use,** (hill top semaphores) **will be adopted.** Clearly with the end of the French wars the Admiralty was reluctant to undertake any new, and expensive initiative in this field. Ronalds reaction was: **I felt very little disappointed and not a shadow of resentment because everyone knows that Telegraphs have long been a great bore at the Admiralty.**[15] However, about the time of his retirement the Admiralty was to have a change of mind as we shall see in a moment.

Ronalds did not develop his telegraph ideas further, but two other pioneering scientists, William Cooke and Charles Wheatstone working along similar lines invented and patented in 1837 a five needle telegraph which was installed alongside the Great Western Railway two years later.[16] The device used electrical impulses sent along a wire insulated from the ground to convey messages by the movements of a needle or a form of early Morse code. This apparatus was then supplanted by the Cooke and Wheatstone two needle telegraph which was cheaper to build and maintain. It was this instrument with an alarm bell which was chosen for use on the new South Western line to Southampton and Gosport.[17] At over 88 miles (55km) this was the longest electric telegraph line then planned in the country.

During its early years the electric telegraph was regarded as primarily a means of sending information, (for railway service work and public use) and not for controlling the movement of trains. At this time there was no link between the signalman and the station telegraph. Cooke had published a report in 1842 setting out how useful his telegraph would be in using it with a form of block working. The line would be divided into blocks, only one train being permitted in each block. A needle telegraph controlling each block would signal line clear or line blocked, i.e. train on line. Early use of the telegraph for this method of train control seems to have been limited to tunnels and single lines.[18]

The telegraph connection with the railway was one of practical convenience, the trackside being the most logical place to site the poles which carried the wires. The station acted as a telegraph office where people could hand in their messages for which there was a charge. Train signal messages known as TAs were given priority, but this was not until much later.[19] Apart from a few exceptions, railway directors were either reluctant to explore the potential the electric telegraph offered for train control, or were put off by the cost. To encourage the establishment of telegraphs alongside railway lines a Government Regulation Act of 1844 required companies to accept it when the Board of Trade issued an order for them to do so. Even so it was well into the 1860s before the telegraph was used widely for railway purposes.[20] It was under this Regulation that a telegraph was built alongside the London & Southampton Railway in 1845.

The advantages of the new telegraph for defence purposes interested the Admiralty who opened negotiations with Messrs. Cooke and Wheatstone and the London & South Western Railway Company to have two of the four proposed telegraph lines on the London to Gosport route for their exclusive use. The total cost of this venture was to be £24,000 split between the Admiralty and the railway company. The Admiralty was to pay £1,500 a year for 21 years to cover maintenance. At the end of this time they could extend the lease or sell their interest at its estimated value which was not to exceed £10,000.[21] Overall not a bad bargain because the staff costs alone for the hill top semaphore system amounted to £5,642 annually and the building and maintenance expenses were extra.[22] There were apparently some changes in the route this telegraph followed. Originally it went from the Nine Elms station in London to Gosport station, into the Clarence Victualling Yard which supplied the warships and under the harbour. In 1848, the telegraph was extended from Nine Elms to the new Waterloo station, from whence it went over Waterloo Bridge and via The Strand and Trafalgar Square to the Admiralty Office in Whitehall. After the London, Brighton & South Coast Railway was opened between Fareham and Cosham in 1848; the telegraph line followed the railway and passed under an arm of the sea (Port Creek) to join the 1847 line from Brighton as far as the Landport (Portsmouth) terminal station (now Portsmouth and Southsea). Here it crossed the fields and fortifications and ended in the Port Admiral's house at the Naval Dockyard.[23]

The Electric Telegraph Company was responsible for supplying and erecting all the posts, and fixing the wires to the insulators. It also furnished the two needle instruments, galvanic batteries and bells at each of the two terminals, and was under contract to maintain the line. Uninsulated copper and galvanised wires were used outdoors. A cotton and pitch composition and gutta percha covering was used for insulation where necessary. Where the lines passed under the sea they were additionally sheathed in rubber and enclosed in lead.

In January 1845 the telegraph line from Gosport to London was ready, tested, and found to be working successfully although there was an unexpected delay of five minutes because the operator at Nine Elms station had fallen asleep in front of the fire whilst awaiting the first transmission.[24]

This chapter began with the Admiralty semaphore stations built on hill tops between London and the coast. Elsewhere semaphore lines were built privately to send commercial information between ports and business centres. The semaphore arms clacking away were part of the landscape in Victorian England, featured in many newspapers, and were familiar to most people.

Sir Charles Hutton Gregory is credited with installing the first two arm semaphore signal at New Cross, London on the London & Croydon railway. Several railway histories suggest that he got the idea from seeing the Admiralty semaphores at work. These were drawn and written about widely, even Charles Dickens describing them as 'wonderful wooden razors'. But as an engineer Gregory would surely have been more influenced by the need for a signal that was highly visible and distinctive. One which would satisfy the fundamental principles of basic signalling which were; to stop the train; instruct the driver to move ahead with caution, and advise him that the line was clear. Simplicity and mechanical reliability were paramount and the semaphore was certainly that. We may never know why Gregory came to prefer the design of the semaphore signal, but it was to endure over other methods. A decade or so later two miniature semaphores were even incorporated into block signalling instruments devised by William Preece. These were used on the London & South Western line as well as widely elsewhere.[26]

In the early years railway signalling was a mish mash of different designs ranging from hand signals to buckets, boards, and shapes.[27] The signals installed by the various companies were based on the views of the engineer, the cost, the safety needs of the line and the volume and speed of trains, not necessarily in this order. To begin with there was little uniformity. When, however, rail tracks multiplied and stations and junctions grew in complexity two types of signal, the disc and the semaphore, emerged as being superior and were adopted by those responsible for train working. Although the Great Western Railway continued to use the disc and crossbar signal designed by Brunel, the Gregory three position semaphore signal soon became standard on the London Brighton & South Coast Railway to Portsmouth. The London & South Western lines had a special revolving disc signal designed by their engineer Albinus Martin, and this was to remain in use for many years. Eventually, however, the Gregory semaphore signal or a variant of it was to be the principal type of signal generally used throughout the entire rail system in Britain.

It seems that the early railway signal engineers failed to take account of the experience the Admiralty had acquired over many years, and their reasons for using semaphore arms instead of other methods. Brunel, in particular, was noted for enforcing his own ideas regardless of the proven experience of others.

The semaphore has been an effective and successful method of signalling for over one hundred and fifty years. Adapted for railway use about 1841 it survived until the introduction of daytime colour light signalling slowly began to supersede it in the 1920s.

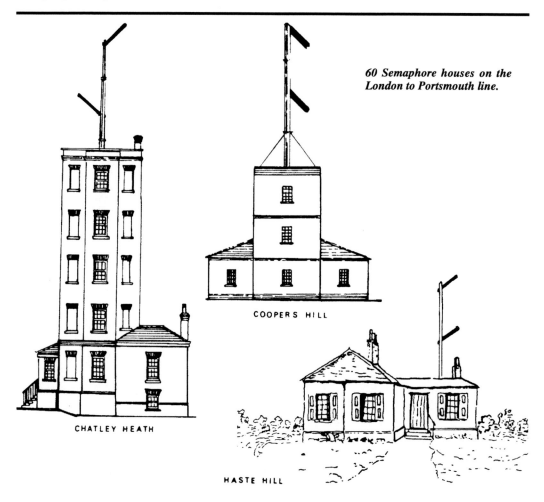

*60 Semaphore houses on the London to Portsmouth line.*

COOPERS HILL

CHATLEY HEATH

HASTE HILL

104

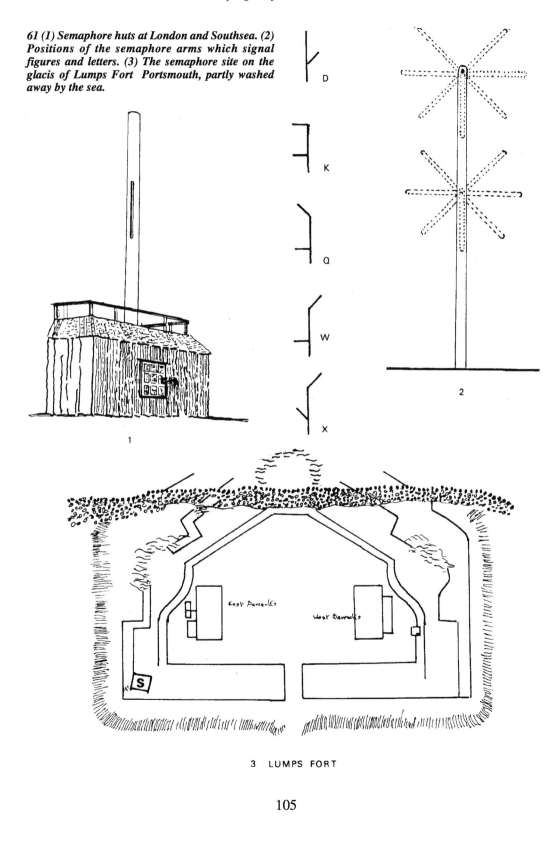

**61 (1) Semaphore huts at London and Southsea. (2) Positions of the semaphore arms which signal figures and letters. (3) The semaphore site on the glacis of Lumps Fort Portsmouth, partly washed away by the sea.**

D

K

Q

W

X

1

2

East Barracks

West Barracks

S

3  LUMPS FORT

105

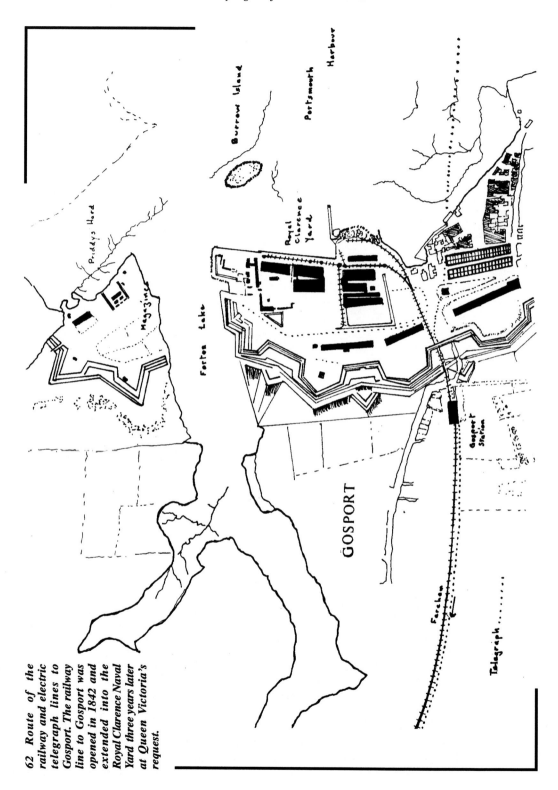

62 Route of the railway and electric telegraph lines to Gosport. The railway line to Gosport was opened in 1842 and extended into the Royal Clarence Naval Yard three years later at Queen Victoria's request.

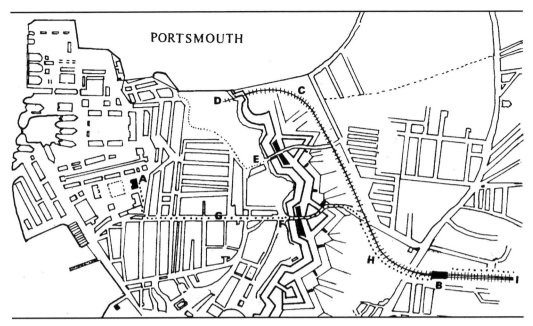

*63 Portsmouth dockyard, railway and electric telegraph. A: Port Admiral's House. B: Portsmouth station. C: Dockyard railway. D: Railway enters dockyard via Sluice Bastion. E: Unicorn Gate. F: Lion Gate. G: Queen Street. H: Probable route of telegraph line. I: Railway to London.*

### The Electric Telegraph

*64 The signal room at Nine Elms terminus London equipped with two double wire telegraph machines for railway use and connected to Gosport station. The smaller single wire machine is for Admiralty use.*

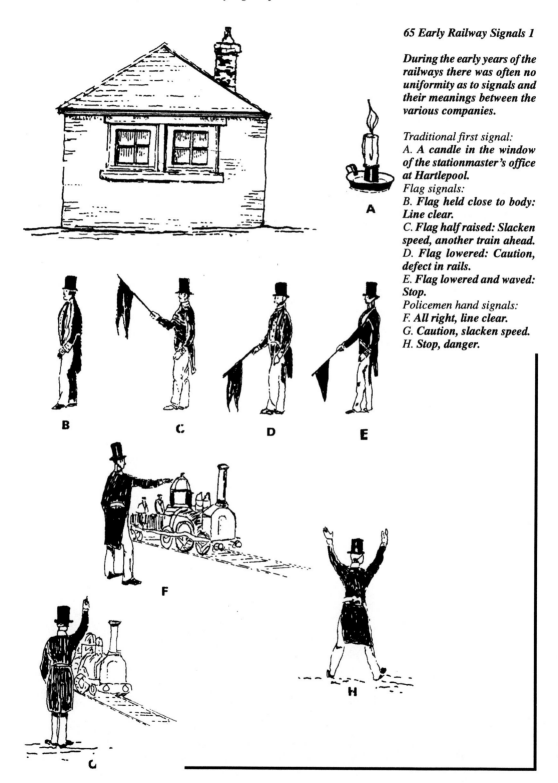

### 65 Early Railway Signals 1

*During the early years of the railways there was often no uniformity as to signals and their meanings between the various companies.*

Traditional first signal:
A. *A candle in the window of the stationmaster's office at Hartlepool.*
Flag signals:
B. **Flag held close to body: Line clear.**
C. **Flag half raised: Slacken speed, another train ahead.**
D. **Flag lowered: Caution, defect in rails.**
E. **Flag lowered and waved: Stop.**
Policemen hand signals:
F. **All right, line clear.**
G. **Caution, slacken speed.**
H. **Stop, danger.**

## 66 Early Railway Signals 2

A *Circular disc turned to line: All Clear.* B *Bucket lowered: Danger. Hoisted: Clear.* C *Aperture on left: Left line clear. Aperture on right: Right line Clear. Aperture at bottom: Both lines blocked. Disc, edge to line: both lines clear.* D *Signal on Grand Junction railway to show line clear or blocked. Sometimes a painted board was used.* E *Disc and cross bar signal used on the Great Western railway.* F *Ball signal at Reading station raised and lowered to show line open and closed.* G *Directional signals used in conjunction with others where lines of different companies met: Great Western and West London lines.*

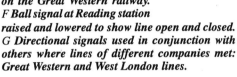

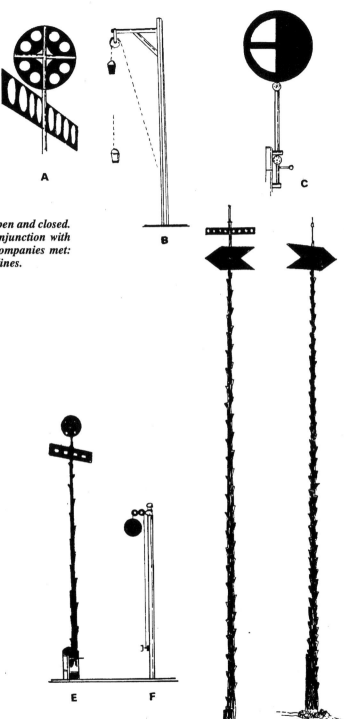

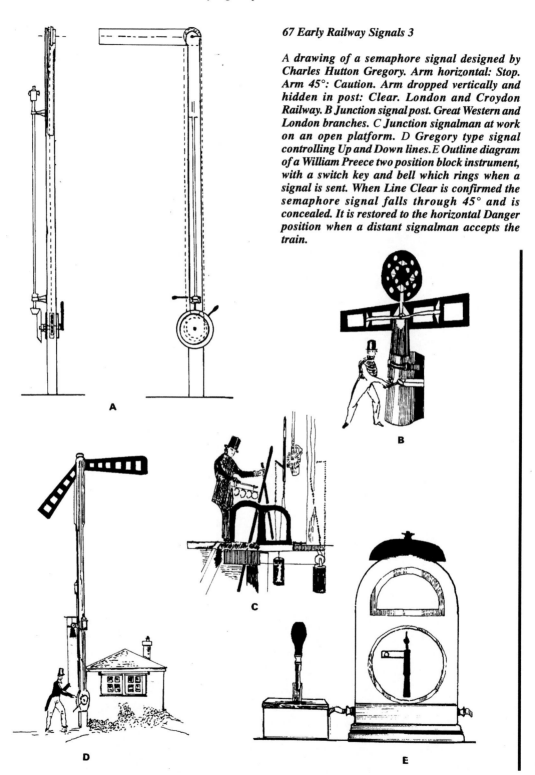

### 67 Early Railway Signals 3

*A drawing of a semaphore signal designed by Charles Hutton Gregory. Arm horizontal: Stop. Arm 45°: Caution. Arm dropped vertically and hidden in post: Clear. London and Croydon Railway. B Junction signal post. Great Western and London branches. C Junction signalman at work on an open platform. D Gregory type signal controlling Up and Down lines. E Outline diagram of a William Preece two position block instrument, with a switch key and bell which rings when a signal is sent. When Line Clear is confirmed the semaphore signal falls through 45° and is concealed. It is restored to the horizontal Danger position when a distant signalman accepts the train.*

A

B

C

D

E

**68. Some types of signal used on early railways, arranged in chronological order.**

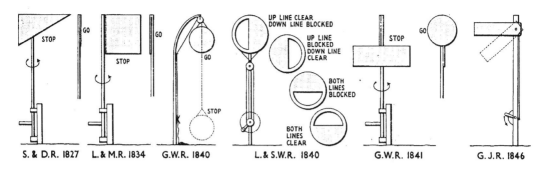

S. & D.R. 1827    L. & M.R. 1834    G.W.R. 1840    L. & S.W.R. 1840    G.W.R. 1841    G.J.R. 1846

**69. Reconstructions of early GWR signals can be seen at the Didcot Railway Centre, adjacent to Didcot station.**

## 70. *Chatley Heath Semaphore Tower*

**The only 19th Century Admiralty Semaphore**
**Tower in Britain open to the Public**

An award winning relic of early naval communication history the Tower, restored by Surrey County Council, is set in 700 acres of wood and heathland with stunning views from London to the North Downs. A visit to the Tower offers:

..Working semaphore demonstrations
..Hands on, replica working models
..Rooftop viewing with telescopes
..Woodland picnic site and amenities

The Tower is usually open between March and September. Telephone the Tower on 01932 862762 or the Countryside Service on 0181 541 9463 for opening times and charges.

The Tower car parks are both situated in Old Lane, close to the A.3.
From the A.3 follow the signs to Effingham.
From the M25 turn off to Guildford and follow signs to Effingham, on the slip road.
From Effingham Junction follow Old Lane right through to the car parks.

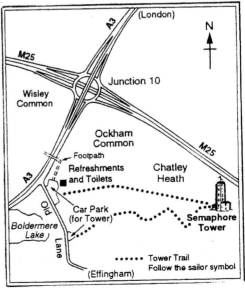

## 71. *How to read semaphore*

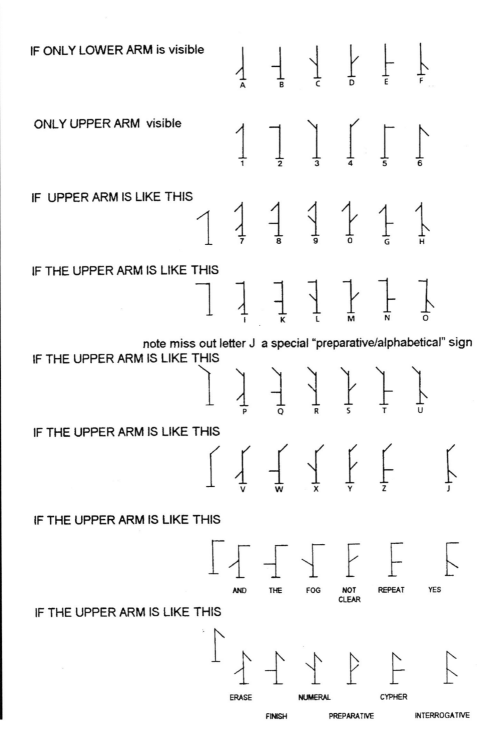

IF ONLY LOWER ARM is visible

A  B  C  D  E  F

ONLY UPPER ARM  visible

1  2  3  4  5  6

IF  UPPER ARM IS LIKE THIS

7  8  9  0  G  H

IF THE UPPER ARM IS LIKE THIS

I  K  L  M  N  O

note miss out letter J  a special "preparative/alphabetical" sign

IF THE UPPER ARM IS LIKE THIS

P  Q  R  S  T  U

IF THE UPPER ARM IS LIKE THIS

V  W  X  Y  Z  J

IF THE UPPER ARM IS LIKE THIS

AND  THE  FOG  NOT CLEAR  REPEAT  YES

IF THE UPPER ARM IS LIKE THIS

ERASE  FINISH  NUMERAL  PREPARATIVE  CYPHER  INTERROGATIVE

113

# NOTES TO SOURCES

**Archive Sources**
BM    British Museum, London
ESRO  East Sussex Record Office, Lewes
NAM  National Army Museum, London
NLS   National Library of Scotland
NMM  National Maritime Museum, London
PRO   Public Records Office, Kew

## Chapter 1 - Early Fire Signals, Smokes and Smothers.
1      Fortescue J.W. Hist. British Army, Vol 1 p.257.
2      Clode C.M. Mil. Forces of the Crown, Vol 1 p262.
3      Clode Vol 1. p.1.
4      Clode Vol 1. p.32.
5      Clode Vol 1. p.282.
6      Williams P. The Tudor Regime. 1979. p.417.
7      Edw 1 c.6. (1285): 1 Edw 3 c.5 (1327).
8      Statute 5 Hen IV c.3. (1403) Watching.
9      Stutt Antiq. Eng. (1775) II.34
10    Armada 1588-1988. Nat. Maritime Museum.1988.
11    State Papers (Domestic) 12 Dec. 1636.
12    White H.T. Archaeologia Cantiana XLVI p.85.
13    Boynton L. Elizabethan Militia, 1588-1638 p.137.
14    State Papers (Domestic) 11 Jul. 1586.
15    Archaeologia Cantiana XLVI p.89.
16    Fletcher A. Sussex 1600-1660 p.191.

## Chapter 2 - The First Admiralty Land Signals
1      Laker J. History of Deal p.284.
2      PRO ADM 12/55 Admiralty Digest, SP
3      Annual Register, 1786 p.94.
4      PRO ADM 3/112 Admiralty Minutes Mar 1794.
5      PRO ADM 3/113  Admiralty Minutes Aug 1794.
6      PRO ADM 3/113 Admiralty Minutes Jun 1794.
7      PRO ADM 1/1620 Capt Clements letters 1795.
8      PRO ADM 1/1620 Capt Clements letters 1795.
9      PRO ADM 12/87 Admiralty Digest, SP.
10    PRO WO 40/16 Treasury letter 1760.
11    PRO ADM 49/112 Letters Vass - Saxton 1803.
12    PRO ADM 12/117 Admiralty Digest, SP. 1805
13    PRO ADM 1/581 Report by Admiral Berkley 1805.
14    PRO ADM 12/139 Admiralty Digest,SP 1809.
15    PRO ADM 12/147 Admiralty Digest, SP 1811.
16    PRO ADM 49/110 Signal Posts closed 1802
17    PRO ADM 49/110  Re-establishment May 1803.
18    PRO ADM 1/4298  Final closure Dec 1815.

## Chapter 3 - Setting up the Land Signal Network.
1      PRO ADM 49/110. Orders and instructions.
2      PRO ADM 1/1620. Clements to Admiralty 1795.
3      PRO ADM 3/112. Admiralty Minutes 27 March 1794.
4      PRO ADM 3/113. Admiralty Minutes 13 August 1794.
5      PRO ADM 3/115. Admiralty Minutes 6 February 1795.
6      PRO ADM 106/1418.Correspondence October 1796.
7      PRO ADM 17/96. Stores for signal stations.

8     PRO ADM 12/63. Report by Mr Vass 19 April 1794.
9     PRO ADM 106/1418. Correspondence October 1796.
10    PRO ADM 49/113. Painting and repair instructions.
11    PRO ADM 49/110. Building plans and costs.
12    PRO ADM 1/1620. Clements to Admiralty 1795.
13    King H.C. History of the Telescope 1955.
14    PRO ADM 49/109. Messrs Dolland to Admiralty 18 April 1804.
15    PRO ADM 106/3125. Order by Committee of Naval Accounts.
16    PRO ADM 49/109. Correspondence with Navy Board 1805.
17    PRO ADM 106/3127. Rents paid for signal sites 1815.
18    PRO ADM 49/110. Reports from Mr Bower and Mr Vass.
19    PRO ADM 12/156. Admiralty Digest entry - signal posts.
20    PRO ADM 12/129. Admiralty Digest entry - signal posts.
21    PRO ADM 12/111. Admiralty Digest entry - signal posts.
22    PRO ADM 1/580. Report by Admiral Berkley 1804.
23    PRO ADM 106/3135. Correspondence 20 June 1805.
24    PRO ADM 49/110. Changes to fuel allowances 1800.
25    PRO ADM 106/3126 Brighton Signal House rebuilt.
26    PRO ADM 106/3127. List of signal posts 1815.

**Chapter 4 - Life and Work in the Naval Signal Stations.**
1     Busk H. Navies of the World 1859.
2     PRO ADM 12/63. Admiralty Digest entry.
3     PRO ADM 49/110. Instructions to Signal Station officers.
4     PRO ADM 1/1620. Capt. Clements to Admiralty 19 May 1795.
5     PRO ADM 49/110; ADM 49/117; ADM 7/974. Pay and fuel grants.
6     PRO ADM 2/135. Admiralty orders 21 March 1798.
7     PRO ADM 106/3125. Standard pattern for Signal Balls.
8     PRO ADM 49/110 Instructions to Signal Station officers.
9     Encyclopaedia Britannica 6th Edition.The Navy.
10    PRO ADM 1/3104. Thomas Read, Kingston Signal Post, 2 Oct 1815.
11    Navy Records Society. Vol 1. Earl St Vincent letters 1810-4.
12    As 11.
13    PRO ADM 1/2755. Reports to Admiralty 1 Aug 1797.
14    PRO ADM 12/147. Admiralty Digest entry.
15    PRO ADM 1/580. Report by Admiral Berkley 31 Dec 1804.
16    PRO ADM 12/83.  Admiralty Digest entry.
17    PRO ADM 12/111. Admiralty Digest entry.
18    PRO ADM 12/111. Admiralty Digest entry.
19    PRO ADM 12/111. Admiralty digest entry.
20    PRO ADM 12/71. Admiralty digest entry.
21    PRO ADM 12/105. Admiralty Digest entry.
22    PRO ADM 12/71. Admiralty Digest entry.
23    Hamilton R.V. Recollections of J.A. Gardner, Navy Records Soc.
24    PRO ADM 12/87. Admiralty Digest entry.
25    PRO ADM 106/3128. Discharge letter to Signal Post officers.

**Chapter 5 - Flying the Flags.**
1     PRO ADM 7/567. King's ships signals to Signal Posts.
2     PRO ADM 2/127. Admiralty Letter to all Signal Posts 8 1794.
3     PRO ADM 49/110. Instructions for Signal Posts 15 Feb. 1804.
4     PRO ADM 1/619. Signals denoting Principal Signal Posts.
5     PRO WO 30/81. Code of signals for use at Signal Posts.
6     ADM 7/589. Admiralty letters Oct.1807; March 1809; Nov.1810.
7     NMM KEI/S/3. Signals between Signal Posts and shore troops.
8     PRO ADM 12/105(Spec). Admirals correspondence 1803.
9     NMM KEI/L73. Lord Keith to Admiralty 21 Feb. 1805.

10      PRO ADM 7/589. Letters on small boat signals 1810.
11      PRO ADM 12/111. Lieut. Hutchinson at Dungeness Signal Post.
12      PRO ADM 12/71. Lieut. John at Lympne Signal Post.
13      The Times newspaper 15 May 1804.
14      PRO ADM 12/134. Admiralty Digest entry - Signal Posts.
15      PRO ADM 12/156. Admiralty digest entry - Signal Posts.
16      PRO ADM 1/3057. Admiralty to Shellness Signal Post.
17      PRO ADM 12/105 (Spec). Admiralty Digest entry - Signal Posts.
18      PRO ADM 1/5114/3. Capt. Owens to Admiralty 6 Jan. 1807
19      Nicholls: Despatches of Lord Nelson. Vol 4 1799-1801.
20      PRO ADM 12/105 (Spec). Admiralty Digest entry - Signal Posts.
21      PRO ADM 12/105 (Spec). Admiralty Digest entry - Signal Posts.
22      PRO HO/394. War Office correspondence Sep.1803.
23      Moore J.C. Dr. Life of Lieut. Gen. John Moore.
24      PRO ADM 1/2755; ADM 12/105. Proposals for signal changes.
25      PRO ADM 12/117. Admiralty Digest entry.
26      PRO ADM 1/2759. Admiralty explains muddle over signals.
27      PRO ADM 7/589. Orders to Signal Posts 6 Nov. 1807 - smugglers.
28      PRO ADM 7/590. Orders to Signal Posts - prisoners of war.

**Chapter 6 - Signals on the Coast at Night.**
1       Coleridge S.T. Ancient Mariner, part VI.1772-1834.
2       PRO ADM 106/1418. Admiralty Corespondence Oct.1796.
3       PRO ADM 49/110. Instructions to Officers at Signal Posts.
4       PRO ADM 106/1418. Summary of comments from signal Posts.
5       PRO ADM 12/87. Admiralty Digest entry - Signal Posts.
6       Faulkener & Burney W. Dictionary of Marine, Blue lights,1815.
7       NMM KEI/S/3. Day and Night Signals - ship to shore.
8       Murray papers Vol 32 (1685) Pierpoint Morgan Library N.York.
9       See 8.
10      PRO ADM 106/3125.Night signals their supply and cost.
11      PRO ADM 17/96. Instructions for making signals at night.
12      PRO ADM 49/114.Correspondence 1804 and diagram 1808.
13      PRO ADM 106/3125. Fire frames, details and costs.
14      PRO ADM 12/87. Difficulties over night signals 1800.
15      Act. 55 Geo 3 cap 128. Signal Stations 1814-15.
16      PRO ADM 12/87. Admiralty Digest entry - Signal Posts.
17      PRO ADM 12/71. Admiralty digest entry - Signal Posts.
18      PRO ADM 12/156. Admiralty Digest entry - Signal Posts.
19      PRO ADM 12/105 (Spec.) Order from Lord Keith 1803. S.P.
20      PRO ADM 7/589. Small Boat 'Private' signals at night. 1810.

**Chapter 7 - Defence of the English Coast in 1803.**
1       PRO WO 30/60 Orders from C.in C. in 1798.
2       PRO WO 30/70 C.in C. orders to generals July 1803.
3       PRO WO 30/81 Gen. Dundas: Communication routes 17 July 1803.
4       PRO ADM 1/4334 Gen. Brownrigg to Sir Nepean at the Admiralty on 21 Dec 1803.
5       PRO WO 133/12 A reference to secret intelligence received on 24 Sep 1803.
6       Lloyd C. Keith Papers, Vol 3. Agreement on beacons at Canterbury 12 Sep 1803.
7       PRO WO 133/12 C.in C. to Gen. Dundas 30 Aug 1803.

**Chapter 8 - Raising the Countryside for War.**
1       NAM 6911-4-7; PRO WO 30/76 Regular, Militia and Volunteers 1804.
2       Glover R. Britain at Bay.C.inC. to Charles Yorke 20 Oct 1803.
3       PRO 30/56  General Dundas to War Dept. 9 Aug 1803.
4       NAM 8108-7 Letter from Somerset Lieutenancy 9 Jul 1803.
5       Lloyd C. Keith Papers Vol 3 1803-15, Navy Record Society.

6     ESRO Act: 43 Geo 3 Cap 55.

7     PRO WO 133/12 War Dept to Dundas 22 and 26 Sep 1803.

8     PRO WO 30/61 Home Dept. to War Dept. 29 Sep 1803.

9     PRO HO 51/74 C.in C. to Lord Edgecombe 1803.

10    PRO WO 1/626 Home Dept. to War Dept. 17 Sep 1803.

11    PRO WO 30/81 General Craig to War Dept. 30 Sep 1803.

12    PRO WO 133/12 War Dept to Craig 26 Sep 1803.

13    PRO WO 30/100 Craig to War Dept. 30 Sep 1803.

14    PRO WO 30/56: HO 50/74 Dundas to War Dept. 9 Aug 1803.

15    The Times 8 Oct and 19 Nov 1803.

16    ESRO SAS/GM: PRO HO 50/72 Sussex and Hampshire 1803.

17    PRO WO 133/12 C.in C. to Dundas 26 Aug 1803.

18    PRO WO 30/56 Bunbary to War Dept. 30 Nov 1803.

19    PRO HO 50/72 Lord Bolton to Yorke 14 Oct 1803.

20    The Times 26 Oct 1803.

21    PRO WO 30/100 Craig to General Milner 10 Sep 1803.

22    The Times 8 Oct: 26 Oct, 1803.

23    PRO WO 30/100 Craig to Milner 10 Sep 1803.

24    PRO WO 30/56 Dundas to War Dept. 9 Aug 1803.

25    PRO WO 133/12 War Dept to Craig 26 Sep 1803.

26    PRO HO 50/72 Bolton to Home Dept. 14 Oct 1803.

27    NAM 6911-4-14: 6911-4-19: 6612-25.Staff at beacons.

28    Hampshire Notes and Queries Vol 9 p.107.Alarm beacons.

29    PRO WO 30/56 Bunbary to War Dept. 30 Nov 1803.

30    PRO WO 30/81 Craig to War Dept. 30 Sep 1803.

31    PRO WO 30/81 War Dept. to General Pulteney 14 Oct 1803.

32    Hamilton Vesey R. Recollections of J.A. Gardner RN.p.251.

33    PRO WO 30/81 Return of Sussex beacon stations 19 Dec 1810.

34    The Times 5 Nov 1803.

35    Hampshire Telegraph and Sussex Chronicle 16 Jan 1804.

36    PRO ADM 1/4335 Decision by William Marsden (Admiralty) 1804.

37    PRO ADM 1/4335 War Dept. to Admiralty 6 Jan 1804.

38    PRO Admiralty Digest entry 7 Jan 1804.

39    PRO ADM 1/4334 War Dept to Admiralty 21 Dec 1803.

40    PRO WO 30/81 Document 6 by Pulteney 22 Jul 1803.

41    PRO WO 30/81 Orders from Dundas 17 Jul 1803.

42    PRO WO 133/12 War Dept. to Craig 26 Sep 1803.

43    PRO ADM 1/2071 Capt Lloyd  and Lord Lieutenants 20 Nov 1803.

44    PRO ADM 1/4335 Comment by Marsden to War Dept.

45    PRO HO 51/74 Home Dept. to Lord Grenville, Lord Lieutenant.

46    PRO WO 30/81 Craig to War Dept. 30 Sep 1803.

47    PRO WO 30/100 Craig to War Dept. 6 Nov 1803.

48    ESRO SAS/GM Regulations signed by Pulteney.

49    PRO ADM 1/4334 War Dept to Admiralty 21 Dec 1803.

50    PRO ADM 2/2638 Admiralty to C.in C. 29 Dec 1803.

51    PRO WO 30/61 General Dalrympne to War Dept. 9 Apr 1804.

52    PRO HO 51/75 Home Dept. to Pulteney 22 Nov 1803.

53    Hampshire Telegraph and Sussex Chronicle 24 Oct 1803.

54    PRO WO 133/12 War Dept. to Dundas 24 Sep 1803.

55    PRO WO 30/81 Return of Sussex beacon stations 19 Dec 1810.

56    Boyden P.B. Fire Beacons. Essex Arch. and History Vol 15 1983

**Chapter 9 - The Earlier History of Military Signals in Southern England.**

1     McCraw Hill: Dictionary of Science and Technology.

2     PRO WO 30/54 York answers questions about defence 1778-80.

3     PRO WO 30/54 Note in Gen. Roy's papers, undated.

4     Philosophical Transactions Vol LXXX 1790.

5     PRO WO 30/75 Gen. Dalrympne to War Dept. 31 Oct 1803.
6     Edgeworth R.L. & M. Memoirs of R.L.E. Vol 2 1820.
7     NMM HOL/49 Gamble J. Essay on Different Modes of Communication.
8     Kerrigan P.M. Castles and Fortifications in Ireland 1996.
9     Encyclopaedia Britannica, Supp. Vol 6, p.648. 1824.
10    PRO ADM 12/67 Admiralty Digest 1795.
11    Fortescue J.W. Hist. of the British Army Vol 4 p.477-479.
12    PRO WO 40/10 Report of Committee March 1798.
13    PRO WO 40/10 York to Wyndham 31 Mar 1798.
14    PRO WO 40/10 Gamble requests orders 18 Apr 1798.
15    PRO WO 40/10 Gen. Brownrigg to Lewis 23 Apr 1798.
16    PRO WO 40/10 Cost of radiated telegraph 18 Apr 1798.
17    Correspondence with Windsor Castle 6 Jan 1997.
18    Hughes G.M. History of Windsor Forest 1890.
19    Riordan T.M. Royal Staff Corps: The Bulletin Nov 1988.
20    PRO WO 30/100 Craig to Brownrigg 6 Nov 1803.
21    As 20.
22    PRO WO 30/67 (1797) and Whites Norfolk Directory 1845.
23    PRO WO 30/100 Craig To Brownrigg 6 Nov 1803.
24    Wilson G. The Old Telegraphs 1976.
25    BM 11th Report Commission to examine public expenditure in Military Departments 1806.
26    BM QMG's evidence in the 11th report 1806.
27    PRO WO 30/100 Craig to War Dept. 6 Nov 1803.
28    PRO WO 30/62 Gen. Morse to Gen. Dundas 21 Aug 1803.
29    PRO ADM 12/104 York to Admiralty 12 Oct 1803.
30    PRO 30/81 Col Smyth's report 1 Oct 1804.
31    PRO MP 1/192 No 1 Sketch of Sussex fieldworks.
32    NAM 6911-4-7 Troops in Sussex 24 Apr 1804.
33    PRO WO 30/81 Col Smyth's report 1 Oct 1804.
34    PRO WO 30/81 Signal Book for officers; undated but references to Sussex military units in 1803.
35    PRO WO 30/81 Instructions for Directors of Telegraphs.
36    PRO WO 40/20 Nepean to Dublin explaining Telegraphic establishments 17 Sep 1804.
37    PRO WO 55/778 Report by Capt. Goldfinch 1 May 1808.
38    PRO WO 30/62 Correspondence with Somerset Dec 1810.
39    PRO ADM 7/589 Admiralty to Somerset Dec 1810.
40    PRO WO 30/81 Admiralty to Somerset Feb 1812.
41    PRO WO 30/81 Document 69. New signals Feb 1812.
42    PRO ADM 7/590 Signals for Martello Tower 27 5 Nov 1812.
43    PRO WO 44/540 Board of Ordnance note 22 Nov 1817.
44    NLS Adv MSS 46-4-22 Murray Papers Vols 68 and 91.
45    Adams R.M. Col. Through to 1970.
46    PRO WO 33/15

## Chapter 10 - The Inland Telegraph Shutter Routes to the Channel Ports.
1    PRO Introductory note to A.12 indexes
2    The Gentlemen's Magazine p.815-816, 11 Sep 1794.
3    Gamble J. Observations on Telegraphic Experiments, 1795.
4    PRO ADM 12/67 Gamble's experiments in 1795.
5    Gamble J. An Essay on Different Modes of Communications by Signals and a History of Progressive Improvements... 1797.
6    PRO ADM 12/63 Murray proposes a Telegraph to Portsmouth.
7    PRO ADM 1/5188 Order in Council 29 Jul 1796.
8    PRO ADM 12/71 Contract to Roebuck 21 Apr 1796.
9    PRO ADM 3/116 Letter to Admiral Peyton 1796.
10    PRO ADM 3/116 Letter to Admiral Buckner 1796.
11    PRO ADM 12/71 Portsmouth Telegraph completed 5 Feb 1796.
12    PRO ADM 3/116 Telegraph to Torbay, Plymouth and Falmouth ordered 15 Apr 1796.

13      See articles in the Gentlemen's Magazine 28 Jan 1796;
        Encyclopedia Britannica 1824; Proceedings of Dorset   Natural History Club Vol Xl, p.135, 1890.
14      Contemporary drawings and models of Shutter Telegraph apparatus differ in details. See New Cross
        Telegraph, (Deptford Library), Blandford Camp Telegraph, ('Through   to 1970' - Royal Signals
        Institution);  and models in the National Maritime Museum, London and Royal Naval Museum,
        Portsmouth.
15      Steel's List. Murray's List. Naval officers and their stations.
16      Holmes T.W. The Semaphore p.44-47, 1983.
17      The Gentlemen's Magazine Vol 66 p.161 28 Jan 1796.
18      Phillips R. Sir, A Morning's Walk, London to Kew, 1820.
19      PRO ADM 1/1087 C.in C. Portsmouth letters.
20      PRO ADM 1/5188 Order in Council 29 Jul 1796.
21      PRO ADM 12/70 Orders to Port Admirals 10 Aug 1796
22      PRO ADM 1/1084 Appointments and promotions 24 Aug 1805.
23      PRO ADM 1/1087 Telegraph message 23 Dec 1805.
24      PRO ADM 1/1018 Telegraph message 11 Aug 1796.
25      PRO ADM 1/1087 Telegraph message 24 Dec 1805.
26      PRO ADM 106/3129 Admiralty to Roebuck 23 Mar 1816.

## Chapter 11 - Semaphores on the South Coast.
1       PRO ADM 1/554 Cmdr. Owen to Lord Keith 13 Jun 1806.
2       Tilloch A. Philosopical Magazine Vol 35 p.389 1810.
3       PRO ADM 1/244 Letters and Estimates Aug 1808-9.
4       PRO ADM 12/147 Navy Board to Admiralty 6 Aug 1810.
5       PRO ADM 7/590 Letter to Lieutenants 9 May 1811.
6       PRO ADM 7/590 Letter to Admiral Young 26 Nov 1811.
7       PRO ADM 106/3125 Semaphore line extension 1812.
8       PRO ADM 106/3125 Admiralty Correspondence 22 Apr 1812.
9       Wilson G. The Old Telegraphs p.34. 1976.
10      PRO ADM 1/4298 Admiralty to Navy Board 30 May 1815.
11      PRO 1/4298 Treasury letters 8 Nov; 8 Dec; 1815.
12      PRO ADM 1/3104 Thomas Read to Admiralty 2;8; Oct 1815.
13      PRO ADM 106/3127 Admiralty to Navy Board 23 Dec 1815.
14      PRO ADM 1/4298 Admiralty to Navy Board 2 Jun 1815.
15      PRO ADM 1/4298 Decision on 2 arm semaphore 23 Dec 1815.
16      PRO ADM 106/3127 Survey reports by Thomas Goddard 1815.
17      PRO ADM 106/3127 Reports, Thomas Edgecombe 10 Aug 1815.
18      PRO ADM 106/3127 Goddard's reports 4 Jan 1816.
19      PRO ADM 106/2269 Navy Board to Admiralty 10 Jun 1816.
20      PRO ADM 12/185 Reports from Port Admirals 26 Feb 1817.
21      PRO ADM 12/185 Admiralty and Treasury letters 1817.
22      Webb W. Official History of HM Coastguard HMSO 1976.
23      PRO ADM 1/4655 Beachy Head to Deal line completed 1820.
24      Geo 3 Cap 128 Admiralty (Signal Stations) Act 1815.
25      PRO ADM 12/194 Prevention of smuggling May 1919.
26      Sussex County Magazine (Customs reports) Vol 4, 1930.
27      PRO ADM 1/2194 Capt. Mingaye to Admiralty Aug 1825.
28      Sussex Advertiser Abolition of Coast Blockade April 1831.
29      PRO ADM 1/2198 Estimates from builders Sep-Nov 1826.

## Chapter 12 - Challenging Changes.
1       PRO ADM 106/349.
2       Popham H. A Damned Cunning Fellow 1991.
3       Tuck O. Fighting Forces Sept 1924.
4       Holmes T.W. The Semaphore 1983.
5       PRO ADM 12/210
6       PRO ADM 12/210.

| | |
|---|---|
| 7 | Holmes T.W. The Semaphore 1983. |
| 8 | PRO ADM 140/656. |
| 9 | Naval Chronicle 1815. |
| 10 | Morriss R. Royal Dockyards in Napoleonic Wars 1983. |
| 11 | Course E. Portsmouth Railways 1972. |
| 12 | Body G. Great Railway Battles 1994. |
| 13 | Goodwin J.F. Military Defence of West Sussex 1985. |
| 14 | Pevsner N; Lloyd D. Buildings of Hampshire and IOW. |
| 15 | Appleyard R. Pioneers of Electrical Communication. |
| 16 | Kieve J.L. Electric Telegraph 1973. |
| 17 | PRO Rail 411/350. |
| 18 | Rolt L.T.C. Red for Danger 1955. |
| 19 | Baker E.C. Sir William Preece, Victorian Engineer. |
| 20 | Thomas D. St. Regional History of Railways of G.B. |
| 21 | PRO Rail 411/350-352: Rail 411/362. |
| 22 | Return to House of Commons 6 Apr 1843. |
| 23 | PRO Rail 411/350. |
| 24 | The Morning Chronicle 25 Jan 1845. |
| 25 | Simmons J. The Victorian Railway 1991. |
| 26 | Baker E.C. Sir William Preece Victorian Engineer. |
| 27 | Parsons J and Cooke B.W. Notes on Railway Signalling 1923. |

# BIBLIOGRAPHY

There are very few books written about the early history of signalling in the army and navy. Fewer still refer to communications between the two services. Occasional articles can be found in some 19th century professional journals, although these often suggest alternative methods rather than those actually being used. There are many more books about railway signalling, (safety engineering), although again its early history has to be pierced together from newspapers and reports often difficult to find. The following list is intended to provide a background to this book which has been mostly written from primary source documents.

**Naval**
Clowes W.L. Sir, The Royal Navy, A history from the earliest times to the present. Vols 4 and 5, 1897
Corbett J.S. Sir. Fighting Instructions 1530-1816, 1971
Corbett J.S. Sir. Signals and Instructions 1776-1794
Encyclopaedia Britannica 6th Edition: Navy, 1824
Falconer W. New Universal Dictionary of the Marine, 1815
Holmes T.W. The Semaphore, 1983
Huddleston R. Coast Signal Stations, Mariners Mirror, July 1911
Jenkins E.H. A History of the French Navy, 1973
Kavanagh M.B. Signal Stations in Jersey, Socit Jersiaise, Vol 20 Part 2, 1970
King H.C. History of the Telescope, 1955
King J.W. The Channel Pilot, Part 1, 1886
Leeson B. Sailing and Fighting Instructions for H.M. Fleet, 1775
Lewis B. The Navy of Britain, 1948
Lloyd C. Mr Barrow of the Admiralty, 1970
Morriss R. The Royal Dockyards in the Revolutionary and Napoleonic Wars, 1983
Navy Record Society. Letters of Lord Vincent 1801-1804 Vols 1 and 2
Navy Record Society. Spencer Papers, 1794-1801, Vol 2, 1914
Navy Record Society. Recollections of James A. Gardner, 1775-1814, Vol 30
Mahan A.T. Influence of Seapower on the French Revolution, 1793-1812, Vol 1 and 2, 1892
Mead H.P. Story of the Semaphore and Naval Telegraph: see volumes of the Mariner's Mirror July 1933-1939
National Maritime Museum. Armada 1588, 1988
Perrin W.G. British Flags, 1922
Popham H. A Dammed Cunning Fellow, 1991
Price A. The Eyes of the Fleet, 1793-1815,
Smyth W.H. Sailor's Word Book of Nautical Terms, 1867
Sockett E.W. Yorkshire Coast War Stations from 1803, Mariner's Mirror, Nov 1991.
Tuck O.The Old Telegraph, Fighting Forces Journal, Sep 1924
Wilson G. The Old Telegraph, 1976


**Military**
Bolton F.J. Capt. Telegraphy for naval and military purposes R.U.S.I. Journal Vol VII,1864
Bunbury H. Sir, Narratives of Some Passages in the War with France 1799-1810, 1854
Floulkes C. Development of Signals for Military Purposes, Society for Army Historical Research Vol 22, 1943
Goodwin J.E. Naval and Military Cooperation over Invasion Warnings 1803, Fortress No 15, 1992
Harris L.H. Brig. Signal Venture (WW1), 1951
HMSO. Army Telegraphy and Telephony Vol 1 & 2, 1909
Jones H.D. Journals of Sieges by the Duke of Wellington 1811-1814 Vol 3, 1846
Kerrigan P.M. Castles and Fortifications in Ireland 1485-1945 1995
Military Panorama or Officer's' Companion - Telegraphic
Signals, 1812
Morrison J.H. Wave to Whisper 1780-1880, 1982
Nalder R.F.H. Royal Corps of Signals. History of
 Antecedents and Development 1800-1995, 1958
Royal Corps of Signals Association - History of Army Communications through to 1970, 1970
Royal Corps of Signals. Short History of Signals in the Army, 1927
Woods D.L. History of Tactical Communications, 1974

**Railways**

Baker E.C. Sir William Preece, Victorian Engineer, 1976
Biddle G. Railway Surveyors
Body G. Great Railway Battles, 1994
Course E. Portsmouth Railways, 1972
Dale R. Early Railways - British Museum
Ellis, C.H. London South Western Railway Mechanical History 1838-1927, 1956
Jackson A.A. London Termini, 1969
Nock O.S. Railways of Britain, 1947
Ottley G. Bibliography of British Railway History, 1983
Oxford Companion to British Railway History, 1997
Parkin A.M. Sir William Preece and the LSWR, South
 Western Circular Vol 8 No 4 October 1989
Parsons J. Cooke B.W. Notes on Railway Signalling
 - Handbook, 1923
Pryer G. Pictorial Record of Southern Signals, 1991
Robertson K. Railways of Gosport, 1986
Robertson K. 150 Years of London South Western Railway
1988
Robbins M. Points and Signals: A Railway Historian at Work, 1967
Rolt L.T.C. Red for Danger, 1995
Sekon G.A. Half a century of Progress to 1896,
Simmons J. The Victorian Railway, 1991
Vanns M.A. Signalling in the Age of Steam, 1995

**Other**

Appleyard R. Pioneers of Electrical Communication, 1929
Austen B. English Provincial Posts 1633-1840, 1978
Kieve J.L. The Electric Telegraph, 1973
Parry J.D. The Coast of Sussex, 1883

# INDEX

1. Numbers in bold refer to maps and illustrations
2. Lt., RN : Lieutenant, Royal Navy.
3. Places of minor significance are not indexed.
4. Note for genealogists: Most Admiralty Signal Posts are linked in the text to the name of the officer in charge. Thus they can be located by name or place. More details are given in Steele's and John Murray's Naval Lists 1795-1814. Also PRO papers: ADM 1/1620 (1795); and ADM 7/591, ADM 49/110, and ADM 106/3135 for 1796 and later years.

**Middleton Press**

If books are not available from your local transport stockist, please order direct from us post free UK.

Easebourne Lane, Midhurst, W Sussex. GU29 9AZ Tel: 01730 813169 Fax: 01730 812601
Email: sales@middletonpress.co.uk   www.middletonpress.co.uk

## BRANCH LINES
Branch Line to Allhallows
Branch Line to Alton
Branch Lines around Ascot
Branch Line to Ashburton
Branch Lines around Avonmouth
Branch Lines around Bodmin
Branch Line to Bude
Branch Lines around Canterbury
Branch Lines around Chard & Yeovil
Branch Line to Cheddar
Branch Lines around Cromer
Branch Line to the Derwent Valley
Branch Lines to East Grinstead
Branch Lines of East London
Branch Lines to Effingham Junction
Branch Lines to Enfield Town & Palace Gates
Branch Lines to Falmouth, Helston & St. Ives
Branch Line to Fairford
Branch Lines to Felixstow & Aldeburgh
Branch Lines around Gosport
Branch Line to Hayling
Branch Lines to Henley, Windsor & Marlow
Branch Line to Hawkhurst
Branch Line to Horsham
Branch Lines around Huntingdon
Branch Line to Ilfracombe
Branch Line to Kingsbridge
Branch Line to Kingswear
Branch Line to Lambourn
Branch Lines to Launceston & Princetown
Branch Lines to Longmoor
Branch Line to Looe
Branch Line to Lyme Regis
Branch Line to Lynton
Branch Lines around March
Branch Lines around Midhurst
Branch Line to Minehead
Branch Line to Moretonhampstead
Branch Lines to Newport (IOW)
Branch Lines to Newquay
Branch Lines around North Woolwich
Branch Line to Padstow
Branch Lines around Plymouth
Branch Lines to Princes Risborough
Branch Lines to Seaton and Sidmouth
Branch Lines around Sheerness
Branch Line to Shrewsbury
Branch Line to Tenterden
Branch Lines around Tiverton
Branch Lines to Torrington
Branch Lines to Tunbridge Wells
Branch Line to Upwell
Branch Line to Wantage (The Wantage Tramway)
Branch Lines of West London
Branch Lines of West Wiltshire
Branch Lines around Weymouth
Branch Lines around Wimborne
Branch Lines around Wisbech

## NARROW GAUGE
Austrian Narrow Gauge
Branch Line to Lynton
Branch Lines around Portmadoc 1923-46
Branch Lines around Porthmadog 1954-94
Branch Line to Southwold
Douglas to Port Erin
Douglas to Peel
Douglas to Ramsey
Hampshire Narrow Gauge
Kent Narrow Gauge
Northern France Narrow Gauge
Romneyrail
Sierra Leone Narrow Gauge
Southern France Narrow Gauge
Sussex Narrow Gauge

Surrey Narrow Gauge
Swiss Narrow Gauge
Two-Foot Gauge Survivors
Vivarais Narrow Gauge

## SOUTH COAST RAILWAYS
Ashford to Dover
Bournemouth to Weymouth
Brighton to Eastbourne
Brighton to Worthing
Dover to Ramsgate
Eastbourne to Hastings
Hastings to Ashford
Ryde to Ventnor
Southampton to Bournemouth

## SOUTHERN MAIN LINES
Basingstoke to Salisbury
Crawley to Littlehampton
Dartford to Sittingbourne
East Croydon to Three Bridges
Epsom to Horsham
Exeter to Barnstaple
Exeter to Tavistock
London Bridge to East Croydon
Tonbridge to Hastings
Salisbury to Yeovil
Sittingbourne to Ramsgate
Swanley to Ashford
Tavistock to Plymouth
Three Bridges to Brighton
Victoria to Bromley South
Victoria to East Croydon
Waterloo to Windsor
Woking to Portsmouth
Woking to Southampton
Yeovil to Exeter

## EASTERN MAIN LINES
Barking to Southend
Ely to Kings Lynn
Ely to Norwich
Fenchurch Street to Barking
Hitchin to Peterborough
Ilford to Shenfield
Ipswich to Saxmundham
Liverpool Street to Ilford
Saxmundham to Yarmouth
Tilbury Loop

## WESTERN MAIN LINES
Banbury to Birmingham
Bristol to Taunton
Didcot to Banbury
Didcot to Swindon
Ealing to Slough
Exeter to Newton Abbot
Moreton-in-Marsh to Worcester
Newton Abbot to Plymouth
Newbury to Westbury
Oxford to Moreton-in-Marsh
Paddington to Ealing
Paddington to Princes Risborough
Plymouth to St. Austell
Princes Risborough to Banbury
Reading to Didcot
Slough to Newbury
St. Austell to Penzance
Swindon to Bristol
Swindon to Newport
Taunton to Exeter
Westbury to Taunton
Worcester to Hereford

## MIDLAND MAIN LINES
Bedford to Wellingborough
Euston to Harrow & Wealdstone
Gloucester to Bristol
Harrow to Watford
St. Albans to Bedford
St. Pancras to St. Albans

## COUNTRY RAILWAY ROUTES
Abergavenny to Merthyr
Andover to Southampton
Bath to Evercreech Junction
Bath Green Park to Bristol
Bournemouth to Evercreech Junction
Brecon to Newport
Burnham to Evercreech Junction
Cheltenham to Andover
Croydon to East Grinstead
Didcot to Winchester
East Kent Light Railway
Fareham to Salisbury
Frome to Bristol
Guildford to Redhill
Reading to Basingstoke
Redhill to Ashford
Salisbury to Westbury
Stratford upon Avon to Cheltenham
Strood to Paddock Wood
Taunton to Barnstaple
Tivetshall to Beccles
Wenford Bridge to Fowey
Westbury to Bath
Woking to Alton
Yeovil to Dorchester

## GREAT RAILWAY ERAS
Ashford from Steam to Eurostar
Festiniog in the Fifties
Festiniog in the Sixties
Festiniog 50 years of enterprise
Isle of Wight Lines 50 years of change
Railways to Victory 1944-46
Return to Blaenau 1970-82
SECR Centenary album
Talyllyn 50 years of enterprise
Wareham to Swanage 50 years of change
Yeovil 50 years of change

## LONDON SUBURBAN RLYS
Caterham and Tattenham Corner
Charing Cross to Dartford
Clapham Jn. to Beckenham Jn.
Crystal Palace (HL) & Catford Loop
East London Line
Finsbury Park to Alexandra Palace
Holborn Viaduct to Lewisham
Kingston and Hounslow Loops
Lewisham to Dartford
Lines around Wimbledon
Liverpool Street to Chingford
Mitcham Junction Lines
North London Line
South London Line
West Croydon to Epsom
West London Line
Willesden Junction to Richmond
Wimbledon to Beckenham
Wimbledon to Epsom

## STEAMING THROUGH
Steaming through Cornwall
Steaming through the Isle of Wight
Steaming through Kent
Steaming through West Hants

## TRAMWAY CLASSICS
Aldgate & Stepney Tramways
Barnet & Finchley Tramways
Bath Tramways
Brighton's Tramways
Bristol's Tramways
Burton & Ashby Tramways
Camberwell & W.Norwood Tramways
Chesterfield Tramways
Clapham & Streatham Tramways
Croydon's Tramways
Derby Tramways
Dover's Tramways
East Ham & West Ham Tramways
Edgware and Willesden Tramways
Eltham & Woolwich Tramways
Embankment & Waterloo Tramways
Exeter & Taunton Tramways
Fulwell – Home to Trams, Trolleys and Buses
Great Yarmouth Tramways
Hammersmith & Hounslow Tramways
Hampstead & Highgate Tramways
Holborn & Finsbury Tramways
Ilford & Barking Tramways
Ilkeston and Glossop Tramways
Kingston & Wimbledon Tramways
Lewisham & Catford Tramways
Liverpool Tramways  1. Eastern Routes
Liverpool Tramways 2. Southern Routes
Liverpool Tramways 3. Northern Routes
Maidstone & Chatham Tramways
Margate to Ramsgate
North Kent Tramways
Norwich Tramways
Reading Tramways
Shepherds Bush & Uxbridge Tramways
Southend-on-sea Tramways
South London Line Tramways 1903-33
Southwark & Deptford Tramways
Stamford Hill Tramways
Twickenham & Kingston Tramways
Victoria & Lambeth Tramways
Waltham Cross & Edmonton Tramways
Walthamstow & Leyton Tramways
Wandsworth & Battersea Tramways

## TROLLEYBUS CLASSICS
Bradford Trolleybuses
Croydon Trolleybuses
Darlington Trolleybuses
Derby Trolleybuses
Huddersfield Trolleybuses
Hull Trolleybuses
Portsmouth Trolleybuses
Reading Trolleybuses

## WATERWAY & SHIPPING
Kent and East Sussex Waterways
London to Portsmouth Waterway
Sussex Shipping - Sail, Steam & Motor
West Sussex Waterways

## MILITARY BOOKS
Battle over Portsmouth
Battle over Sussex 1940
Blitz over Sussex 1941-42
Bombers over Sussex 1943-45
Bognor at War
East Ridings Secret Resistance
Military Defence of West Sussex
Military Signals from the South Coast
Secret Sussex Resistance
Sussex Home Guard
Surrey Home Guard

## OTHER RAILWAY BOOKS
Collectors for Trains, Trolleys & Trams
Industrial Railways of the South-East
South Eastern & Chatham Railways
London Chatham & Dover Railway
London Termini - Past and Proposed
War on the Line (SR 1939-45)